Key Stage 2

Practice

Hilary Koll and Steve Mills

Name *Lights*

Schofield & Sims

Introduction

Understanding Maths Practice lets you practise aspects of the maths curriculum: addition, subtraction, multiplication, division, fractions, decimals, percentages, number patterns, algebra, problem solving, geometry, measurement and statistics. All of these topics are linked. For example, your multiplication skills will help you to answer problem solving questions, and your understanding of addition will enable you to solve simple algebra questions.

How to use this book

Before you start using this book, write your name in the box on the first page.

Then decide how to begin. If you want practice on all addition and subtraction, for example, you should work through that section from beginning to end. If you just want more practice on subtraction, then choose the subtraction questions from that section.

To practise all the topics in this book, do question 1 from each of the sections, followed by question 2 and so on. You will find that each section starts with easier questions and gradually becomes more difficult.

Whichever way you choose, don't try to do too much at once – it's better to tackle the questions in short bursts. You might find it useful to have some spare paper to work on for some of the activities.

For help with any of the topics, look at the red box at the bottom of each page:

> **For help with the questions on this page see**
> *Understanding Maths: Addition & Subtraction* **pages 10–12.**

This tells you which other **Understanding Maths** study books will help you and where in those books to find the relevant help.

Answers

Answers to the questions can be found at the end of the book (pages 73–88). Use this to help you to mark your work as you go along.

Make a note of any questions or topics you found difficult and use the other **Understanding Maths** study books to help you with these.

Contents

Tick the box when you have worked through the topic.

Addition & Subtraction

1 Add these multiples of **5**.

    a 35 + 5 = _____   **b** 25 + 15 = _____   **c** 35 + 25 = _____

    d 25 + 75 = _____   **e** 35 + 65 = _____   **f** 55 + 45 = _____

2 Fill in the missing numbers.

    a 15 + ☐ = 100   **b** 35 + ☐ = 100

    c 75 + ☐ = 100   **d** 90 + ☐ = 100

3 Fill in the missing numbers.

    a 200 + 800 = ☐   **b** 400 + 600 = ☐

    c 700 + ☐ = 1000   **d** 100 + ☐ = 1000

4 Find the total for each row and column.

a

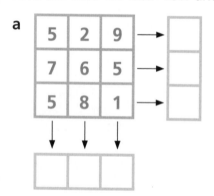

b

3	8	7
5	7	8
7	9	2

5 Find the total for each row and column.

a

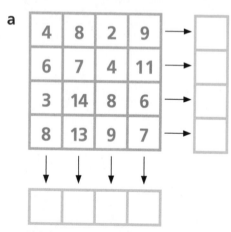

b

8	2	7	5
14	6	9	4
7	12	3	9
6	8	13	7

For help with the questions on this page see
Understanding Maths: Addition & Subtraction **pages 4–7.**

Addition & Subtraction

6 Follow the steps to find the answers, like this: $12 + 8 - 6 + 7 - 8 + 6 - 7 =$ _____

a [12]─[add **8**]─[subtract **6**]─[add **7**]─[subtract **8**]─[add **6**]─[subtract **7**] _____

b [19]─[subtract **13**]─[add **9**]─[subtract **7**]─[add **7**]─[subtract **9**]─[add **13**] _____

c [28]─[add **18**]─[subtract **14**]─[add **15**]─[subtract **18**]─[add **14**]─[subtract **15**] _____

d [36]─[subtract **19**]─[add **14**]─[subtract **11**]─[add **19**]─[subtract **14**]─[add **11**] _____

7 What do you notice about each of your answers? Why do you think this is?

_____

_____

8 Use these addition and subtraction facts to help you answer the questions below.

[$33 + 19 = 52$]   [$17 + 29 = 46$]   [$39 - 24 = 15$]

a $46 - 29 =$ _____   **b** $24 + 15 =$ _____   **c** $52 - 33 =$ _____

9 Choose a number from the box.
Double your number, then add
one and subtract one.

[21   24   36   27   32
   45   23   49   38]

Write your answers on some spare paper.
Do this for all the numbers in the box.

[**Double 27 = 54** ─-1→ **53**
                     ─$+1$→ **55**]

Now use your answers to solve these.

a $24 + 23 =$ _____   **b** $32 + 31 =$ _____   **c** $21 + 22 =$ _____

d $23 + 22 =$ _____   **e** $38 + 39 =$ _____   **f** $49 + 48 =$ _____

g $210 + 220 =$ _____   **h** $360 + 370 =$ _____   **i** $320 + 330 =$ _____

For help with the questions on this page see
Understanding Maths: Addition & Subtraction **pages 8–9.**

Addition & Subtraction

10 Look for patterns to help you answer these questions.

a 26 + 7 = _____

    36 + 7 = _____

    46 + 7 = _____

b 19 + 16 = _____

    19 + 26 = _____

    19 + 36 = _____

c 23 − 14 = _____

    33 − 14 = _____

    43 − 14 = _____

d   5 +   7 = _____

    50 + 70 = _____

   500 + 700 = _____

e   9 +   6 = _____

   90 + 60 = _____

  900 + 600 = _____

f   10 − 9 = _____

   100 − 9 = _____

  1000 − 9 = _____

11 Use the diagrams to add these numbers.

a
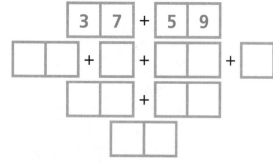

b
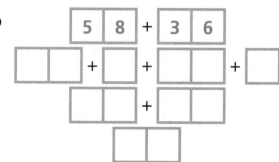

c
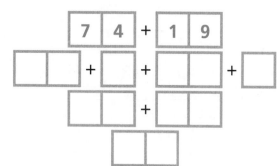

d
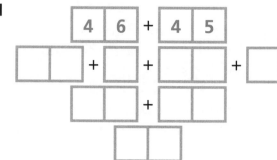

12 Try these, using a similar method, in your head.

a 19 + 46 = _____

b 37 + 28 = _____

c 18 + 59 = _____

d 38 + 56 = _____

e 49 + 38 = _____

f 76 + 55 = _____

For help with the questions on this page see
Understanding Maths: Addition & Subtraction **pages 10–12.**

Addition & Subtraction

13 Find the difference between these numbers by counting on.

a **18** and **27** = _____ b **37** and **56** = _____ c **63** and **82** = _____

d **69** and **94** = _____ e **88** and **105** = _____ f **93** and **113** = _____

14 Answer these questions by counting on.

a $105 - 96 =$ _____ b $207 - 198 =$ _____ c $304 - 296 =$ _____

d $409 - 397 =$ _____ e $407 - 396 =$ _____ f $503 - 492 =$ _____

15 Add these numbers.

a $47 + 19 =$ _____ b $37 + 12 =$ _____ c $58 + 23 =$ _____

d $19 + 142 =$ _____ e $218 + 27 =$ _____ f $341 + 38 =$ _____

g $514 + 37 =$ _____ h $39 + 487 =$ _____ i $623 + 59 =$ _____

j $215 + 99 =$ _____ k $304 + 99 =$ _____ l $481 + 99 =$ _____

m $276 + 103 =$ _____ n $102 + 274 =$ _____ o $385 + 199 =$ _____

p $476 + 199 =$ _____ q $683 + 205 =$ _____ r $197 + 784 =$ _____

16 Subtract these numbers.

a $63 - 19 =$ _____ b $77 - 21 =$ _____ c $98 - 23 =$ _____

d $364 - 62 =$ _____ e $532 - 49 =$ _____ f $628 - 59 =$ _____

g $158 - 99 =$ _____ h $217 - 99 =$ _____ i $382 - 101 =$ _____

j $658 - 299 =$ _____ k $703 - 304 =$ _____ l $865 - 307 =$ _____

17 Use partitioning to add these numbers. Do your working out on some spare paper.

a $315 + 26 =$ _____ b $476 + 54 =$ _____ c $568 + 73 =$ _____

d $547 + 162 =$ _____ e $838 + 283 =$ _____ f $612 + 476 =$ _____

For help with the questions on this page see
Understanding Maths: Addition & Subtraction **pages 13–18.**

18 Use partitioning to subtract these numbers. Use spare paper for your working.

a 285 – 43 = _____   b 478 – 56 = _____   c 589 – 76 = _____

d 527 – 214 = _____   e 769 – 538 = _____   f 964 – 743 = _____

g 265 – 57 = _____   h 538 – 46 = _____   i 473 – 81 = _____

j 614 – 284 = _____   k 753 – 376 = _____   l 964 – 687 = _____

19 Answer these questions using any method.

a 651 – 53 = _____   b 683 – 49 = _____

c 676 – 94 = _____   d 542 – 396 = _____

e 653 – 576 = _____   f 912 – 759 = _____

g 53 373 + 1396 = _____   h 7386 + 21 237 = _____

i 47 675 + 4792 = _____   j 62 709 + 28 346 = _____

k 29 867 – 2745 = _____   l 64 756 – 29 594 = _____

m 72 251 – 57 512 = _____   n 84 492 – 49 994 = _____

20 Here is a list of attendances at some Premiership football matches.

Match **1**	Liverpool v Arsenal	**54 118**
Match **2**	Birmingham v Everton	**32 809**
Match **3**	Man United v Spurs	**75 046**
Match **4**	Newcastle U v Bolton W	**51 008**
Match **5**	Aston Villa v Chelsea	**40 385**
Match **6**	Blackburn R v Portsmouth	**27 985**

Find the difference between the attendances at these matches. Remember to put the larger number first.

a Match **1** and Match **4** _____   b Match **2** and Match **6** _____

c Match **3** and Match **5** _____   d Match **4** and Match **6** _____

e Match **3** and Match **6** _____   f Match **5** and Match **4** _____

For help with the questions on this page see
Understanding Maths: Addition & Subtraction pages 20–26.

Addition & Subtraction

21 Write an approximation for each of these additions or subtractions.

a 3878 + 2053 = _____

_____ + _____ = _____

b 6931 − 3855 = _____

_____ − _____ = _____

c 8865 − 4121 = _____

_____ − _____ = _____

d 3185 + 4853 = _____

_____ + _____ = _____

22 Now answer each of the calculations in question 21.

23 Now check each answer by doing an inverse calculation. Write the calculations here.

a _____

b _____

c _____

d _____

24 Find each missing number.

a 7534 − ☐ = 2343

b 3684 + ☐ = 9645

c ☐ + 3126 = 8753

d ☐ − 1764 = 6643

25 Find these totals.

a 343 + 475 + 44 = _____

b 5634 + 33 + 365 = _____

c 3564 + 85 + 443 = _____

d 2615 + 3853 + 45 = _____

For help with the questions on this page see
Understanding Maths: Addition & Subtraction **pages 28–30.**

Addition & Subtraction

26 Write the value of the digit **2** in each number.

    a 48 424 _____

    b 738 952 _____

    c 8 215 664 _____

    d 126 883 _____

    e 2 871 849 _____

    f 1 782 045 _____

27 Write these numbers in figures.

    a four million, seven hundred and seven thousand, one hundred and six _____

    b nine million, one hundred and eleven thousand, eight hundred and ten _____

    c two million, twelve thousand and forty-five _____

28 Answer these additions.

    a $800\,000 + 30\,000 + 8000 + 500 + 10 + 2 =$ _____

    b $4\,000\,000 + 40\,000 + 2000 + 8 =$ _____

29 Answer these additions using place value ideas.

    a $353\,244 + 101\,001 =$ _____

    b $432\,817 + 21\,040 =$ _____

    c $426\,117 + 33\,040 =$ _____

    d $450\,252 + 203\,005 =$ _____

    e $1\,272\,144 + 303\,004 =$ _____

    f $344\,003 + 1\,101\,005 =$ _____

30 Answer these subtractions using place value ideas.

    a $588\,248 - 33\,001 =$ _____

    b $367\,851 - 201\,040 =$ _____

    c $1\,556\,235 - 101\,001 =$ _____

    d $962\,893 - 401\,003 =$ _____

For help with the questions on this page see
Understanding Maths: Addition & Subtraction pages 31–32.

Addition & Subtraction

31 Add these numbers.

a
```
    3 7 . 7 2
  + 4 1 . 0 9
  _____
```

b
```
    5 6 . 1 8
  + 3 2 . 8 6
  _____
```

c
```
    6 5 . 3 4
  + 2 8 . 4 7
  _____
```

32 Add these amounts of money.

a
```
    £ 4 1 . 5 6
  + £ 2 9 . 3 2
  _____
```

b
```
    £ 5 3 . 7 6
  + £ 2 9 . 6 8
  _____
```

c
```
    £ 5 7 . 3 9
  + £ 3 6 . 4 6
  _____
```

33 Subtract these numbers.

a
```
    2 8 . 7
  - 1 7 . 2
  _____
```

b
```
    5 2 . 1 8
  - 3 7 . 6 6
  _____
```

c
```
    8 3 . 6 5
  - 3 9 . 8 7
  _____
```

34 Subtract these amounts of money.

a
```
    £ 3 9 . 6 5
  - £ 2 4 . 3 1
  _____
```

b
```
    £ 6 2 . 1 7
  - £ 3 2 . 3 8
  _____
```

c
```
    £ 9 4 . 0 2
  - £ 3 7 . 8 1
  _____
```

35 **8149** people visited the ice rink this year. This was **1728** less than last year. How many people visited the ice rink last year? _____

36 Mei buys a chocolate bar for **37**p, a drink for **41**p and a newspaper for £**1.65**. How much change does she get from £**5**? _____

37 A garden centre has **8329** plant pots. **5607** are empty. How many plants in pots are there in the garden centre? _____

For help with the questions on this page see
Understanding Maths: Addition & Subtraction **pages 33–37.**

38 Answer these problems mentally.

a An adult giraffe is **5850**mm tall. A new-born giraffe is **4020**mm shorter. How tall is the new-born giraffe?

_____

b Two TVs are for sale. One costs £**512** more than the other. If the cheaper TV costs £**1226**, what does the more expensive one cost?

_____

c There were **5738** men and **3030** women at a hockey match. How many adults were there altogether?

_____

39 Answer these two-step problems.

a Jasmine has £**77.45** in her wallet and £**84.67** in her bank account. She uses her money to buy a computer game that costs £**121.56**. How much money does she have now?

_____

b A famous tennis player earns £**7 614 743** in one year. In the previous year she earnt £**356 478** less. How much does she earn in the two years put together?

_____

40 Solve these problems.

a Adam joins four lengths of wood together, end-to-end. One is **15.7**cm long, one is **0.4**m long, one is **0.13**m long and the fourth is **28**cm long. How long is that altogether?

_____

b I have three bags of sweets. One weighs **250**g, one weighs **0.8**kg and the third weighs **278.9**g. How much do they weigh altogether?

_____

c Laura weighs two suitcases ready for a flight. One suitcase weighs **19.7**kg and the other weighs **1500**g more than this. What is the total weight of the suitcases?

_____

For help with the questions on this page see
Understanding Maths: Addition & Subtraction **pages 37–40.**

Multiplication & Division

1 Answer these questions.

a $10 \times 5 =$ ____ b $5 \times 10 =$ ____ c $4 \times 7 =$ ____ d $7 \times 4 =$ ____

e $3 \times 9 =$ ____ f $9 \times 3 =$ ____ g $5 \times 6 =$ ____ h $6 \times 5 =$ ____

i $12 \div 2 =$ ____ j $10 \div 5 =$ ____ k $9 \div 3 =$ ____ l $20 \div 5 =$ ____

m $20 \div 4 =$ ____ n $12 \div 3 =$ ____ o $15 \div 5 =$ ____ p $16 \div 2 =$ ____

2 Use these multiplication and division facts to help you answer the questions below.

| $4 \times 5 = 20$ | $20 \div 2 = 10$ | $4 \times 4 = 16$ |
| $21 \div 3 = 7$ | $10 \times 5 = 50$ | $30 \div 5 = 6$ |

a $20 \div 5 =$ _____ b $50 \div 5 =$ _____ c $2 \times 10 =$ _____

d $5 \times 6 =$ _____ e $16 \div 4 =$ _____ f $7 \times 3 =$ _____

3 Test yourself on these questions.

$3 \times 9 =$ _____ $4 \times 8 =$ _____ $0 \times 9 =$ _____ $4 \times 7 =$ _____

$9 \times 10 =$ _____ $10 \times 8 =$ _____ $2 \times 3 =$ _____ $3 \times 8 =$ _____

$5 \times 5 =$ _____ $4 \times 3 =$ _____ $4 \times 5 =$ _____ $5 \times 8 =$ _____

$3 \times 7 =$ _____ $5 \times 3 =$ _____ $4 \times 2 =$ _____ $4 \times 9 =$ _____

$3 \times 10 =$ _____ $5 \times 9 =$ _____ $10 \times 4 =$ _____ $2 \times 9 =$ _____

$2 \times 6 =$ _____ $4 \times 4 =$ _____ $3 \times 6 =$ _____ $4 \times 6 =$ _____

$5 \times 7 =$ _____ $2 \times 8 =$ _____ $2 \times 5 =$ _____ $3 \times 5 =$ _____

For help with the questions on this page see
Understanding Maths: Multiplication & Division pages 4–7 and 14–15.

Multiplication & Division

4 Write the first 12 multiples of **3**.

_____ _____ _____ _____ _____ _____ _____ _____ _____ _____ _____ _____

5 Answer these division questions.

a 27 ÷ 3 = ____   **b** 24 ÷ 2 = ____   **c** 30 ÷ 5 = ____   **d** 60 ÷ 10 = ____

e 32 ÷ 4 = ____   **f** 45 ÷ 5 = ____   **g** 21 ÷ 3 = ____   **h** 18 ÷ 2 = ____

i 110 ÷ 10 = ____   **j** 33 ÷ 3 = ____   **k** 22 ÷ 2 = ____   **l** 24 ÷ 4 = ____

6 Answer these questions.

a Divide **80** by **10**.   _____

b How many teams of four are there in **36**?   _____

c What is **35** split equally between five?   _____

d What is the product of **5** and **9**?   _____

e How many is **12** groups of four?   _____

7 Answer these problems.

a There are two avocados in each pack. How many avocados are there in seven packs?   _____

b **27** children get into teams of three. How many teams are there?   _____

c Leo runs **10**km every day for seven days. How far does he run altogether?   _____

8 Double these numbers.

a 17 ____   **b** 24 ____   **c** 32 ____   **d** 46 ____   **e** 48 ____

f 54 ____   **g** 67 ____   **h** 73 ____   **i** 86 ____   **j** 95 ____

For help with the questions on this page see
Understanding Maths: Multiplication & Division pages 8–12.

Multiplication & Division

9   Test yourself on these questions.

$8 \times 9 = $ _____	$9 \times 9 = $ _____	$9 \times 5 = $ _____	$8 \times 6 = $ _____
$6 \times 5 = $ _____	$10 \times 9 = $ _____	$6 \times 7 = $ _____	$7 \times 8 = $ _____
$7 \times 7 = $ _____	$6 \times 6 = $ _____	$7 \times 4 = $ _____	$8 \times 7 = $ _____
$9 \times 8 = $ _____	$7 \times 10 = $ _____	$9 \times 6 = $ _____	$7 \times 5 = $ _____
$8 \times 8 = $ _____	$9 \times 7 = $ _____	$8 \times 3 = $ _____	$7 \times 9 = $ _____
$6 \times 3 = $ _____	$8 \times 5 = $ _____	$6 \times 9 = $ _____	$6 \times 8 = $ _____

10   Test yourself on these questions.

$27 \div 9 = $ _____	$36 \div 9 = $ _____	$40 \div 8 = $ _____	$42 \div 6 = $ _____
$35 \div 7 = $ _____	$32 \div 8 = $ _____	$45 \div 9 = $ _____	$42 \div 7 = $ _____
$48 \div 8 = $ _____	$36 \div 6 = $ _____	$56 \div 7 = $ _____	$70 \div 10 = $ _____
$48 \div 6 = $ _____	$63 \div 9 = $ _____	$72 \div 8 = $ _____	$100 \div 10 = $ _____
$72 \div 9 = $ _____	$56 \div 8 = $ _____	$54 \div 9 = $ _____	$64 \div 8 = $ _____
$54 \div 6 = $ _____	$63 \div 7 = $ _____	$49 \div 7 = $ _____	$81 \div 9 = $ _____

11   Answer these multiplications and divisions.

a $4 \times 11 = $ ____	**b** $7 \times 12 = $ ____	**c** $6 \times 11 = $ ____	**d** $8 \times 12 = $ ____
e $88 \div 11 = $ ____	**f** $36 \div 12 = $ ____	**g** $33 \div 11 = $ ____	**h** $60 \div 12 = $ ____
i $132 \div 11 = $ ____	**j** $11 \times 11 = $ ____	**k** $12 \times 12 = $ ____	**l** $12 \div 12 = $ ____
m $9 \times 11 = $ ____	**n** $9 \times 12 = $ ____	**o** $96 \div 12 = $ ____	**p** $120 \div 12 = $ ____
q $10 \times 11 = $ ____	**r** $6 \times 12 = $ ____	**s** $108 \div 12 = $ ____	**t** $121 \div 11 = $ ____

> **For help with the questions on this page see**
> *Understanding Maths: Multiplication & Division* **pages 9 and 14–16.**

Multiplication & Division

12 Find each missing number.

a 24 ÷ ☐ = 4

b 12 × ☐ = 60

c ☐ × 9 = 81

d ☐ ÷ 4 = 8

13 Find each missing number.

a 11 ÷ ☐ = 11

b 1 × ☐ = 12

c ☐ × 6 = 6

d ☐ ÷ 4 = 4

14 To answer these questions, **double** the first number and **halve** the other.

a [10] × [7]
5 × 14 = ___70___

b ☐ × ☐
5 × 16 = _____

c ☐ × ☐
5 × 18 = _____

d ☐ × ☐
5 × 26 = _____

e ☐ × ☐
5 × 28 = _____

f ☐ × ☐
5 × 40 = _____

15 Multiply these numbers by **10**.

a 8 → _____

b 23 → _____

c 39 → _____

d 75 → _____

e 216 → _____

f 462 → _____

g 589 → _____

h 4208 → _____

i 6290 → _____

16 Change these prices from pounds to pence by multiplying by **100**.

a £5 → _____

b £18 → _____

c £76 → _____

d £254 → _____

e £1968 → _____

f £2097 → _____

For help with the questions on this page see
Understanding Maths: Multiplication & Division pages 17–21.

Practice

Multiplication & Division

17 Answer these questions.

a $8 \times 3 \times 5 =$ _____

b $6 \times 4 \times 5 =$ _____

c $7 \times 4 \times 2 =$ _____

d $8 \times 8 \times 5 =$ _____

e $5 \times 3 \times 3 \times 1 =$ _____

f $6 \times 8 \times 5 \times 0 \times 3 \times 5 =$ _____

18 Divide these numbers by **10**.

a 80 → _____

b 120 → _____

c 390 → _____

d 470 → _____

e 780 → _____

f 950 → _____

g 3870 → _____

h 4280 → _____

i 9850 → _____

19 Change these prices from pence to pounds by dividing by **100**.

a 200p → _____

b 600p → _____

c 800p → _____

d 1500p → _____

e 2300p → _____

f 4500p → _____

g 5600p → _____

h 25 700p → _____

i 50 000p → _____

20 Change these lengths from centimetres to metres by dividing by **100**.

a 400cm → _____

b 750cm → _____

c 1250cm → _____

d 3400cm → _____

e 6800cm → _____

f 8700cm → _____

g 9100cm → _____

h 54 800cm → _____

i 320 800cm → _____

21 Answer these questions, using doubling and halving.

a $7 \times 2 =$ ____

b $8 \times 4 =$ ____

c $25 \times 2 =$ ____

d $25 \times 4 =$ ____

e $48 \div 2 =$ ____

f $32 \div 4 =$ ____

g $64 \div 2 =$ ____

h $64 \div 4 =$ ____

> **For help with the questions on this page see**
> *Understanding Maths: Multiplication & Division* **pages 19 and 22–25.**

22 Use a column method to multiply these numbers.

a
```
    8 3
×     5
  ─────
```

b
```
    5 7
×     6
  ─────
```

c
```
    6 9
×     4
  ─────
```

23 Write the answers.

a $400 \times 2 =$ _____

b $300 \times 4 =$ _____

c $500 \times 8 =$ _____

d $700 \times 6 =$ _____

24 Use partitioning to multiply these numbers.

a $433 \times 3 =$ _____

b $321 \times 4 =$ _____

c $414 \times 5 =$ _____

d $506 \times 7 =$ _____

25 Answer these questions. Give a remainder.

a $16 \div 3 =$ _5 r1_

b $10 \div 3 =$ _____

c $19 \div 3 =$ _____

d $25 \div 3 =$ _____

e $29 \div 3 =$ _____

f $31 \div 3 =$ _____

g $18 \div 4 =$ _____

h $25 \div 4 =$ _____

i $30 \div 4 =$ _____

j $35 \div 4 =$ _____

k $37 \div 4 =$ _____

l $43 \div 4 =$ _____

26 Answer these division questions.

a $55 \div 5 =$ _____

b $\frac{1}{3}$ of **27** = _____

c $6\overline{)42}$

d $7\overline{)35}$

For help with the questions on this page see
Understanding Maths: Multiplication & Division pages 26–30.

27 Write the answers.

a $4 \times 4 =$ _____   b 5 squared = _____   c $10^2 =$ _____

d $2 \times 2 \times 2 =$ _____   e 5 cubed = _____   f $10^3 =$ _____

28 Answer these questions.

a Find the answer to **14 × 8** by splitting **14** into **5** and **9**.

$5 \times 8 =$ _____ and $9 \times 8 =$ _____ so $14 \times 8 =$ _____

b Find the answer to **13 × 7** by splitting **13** into **8** and **5**.

$8 \times 7 =$ _____ and $5 \times 7 =$ _____ so $13 \times 7 =$ _____

29 Find the area of each of these rectangles, splitting the larger number to make the multiplication easier.

a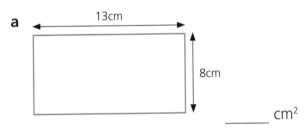
_____ cm²

b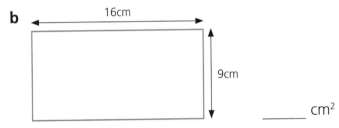
_____ cm²

30 Use a column method to answer these.

a
```
    4  6  3
×         3
_____

_____
```

b
```
    5  2  7
×         5
_____

_____
```

c
```
    4  8  6
×         4
_____

_____
```

d
```
    1  8  8
×         7
_____

_____
```

e
```
    4  3  9
×         8
_____

_____
```

f
```
    2  8  3
×         9
_____

_____
```

For help with the questions on this page see
Understanding Maths: Multiplication & Division **pages 31–35.**

Multiplication & Division

31 Answer these using short multiplication.

   a $5 \times 463 =$ _____   **b** $4 \times 572 =$ _____   **c** $486 \times 6 =$ _____

   d $4 \times 357 =$ _____   **e** $5 \times 618 =$ _____   **f** $726 \times 6 =$ _____

32 Answer these using short multiplication.

   a $2356 \times 5 =$ _____   **b** $6219 \times 7 =$ _____   **c** $8 \times 7472 =$ _____

   d $3186 \times 4 =$ _____   **e** $5429 \times 7 =$ _____   **f** $8 \times 6374 =$ _____

33 Try these questions.

   a $5 \overline{)135}$ **b** $6 \overline{)138}$ **c** $7 \overline{)147}$

   d $6 \overline{)378}$ **e** $5 \overline{)235}$ **f** $8 \overline{)456}$

34 Answer these divisions, using short division.

   a $3 \overline{)6342}$ **b** $4 \overline{)8644}$

   c $5 \overline{)8075}$ **d** $3 \overline{)4497}$

For help with the questions on this page see
Understanding Maths: Multiplication & Division **pages 35–38.**

Multiplication & Division

35 Write an approximation for each of these multiplications or divisions.

    a $193 \times 4 =$ _____   b $215 \div 5 =$ _____

    _____ $\times$ _____ $=$ _____   _____ $\div$ _____ $=$ _____

36 Now answer each of the calculations in question 35.

37 Now check each answer by doing an inverse calculation. Write the calculations here.

    a _____   b _____

38 Answer these division questions, using short division, giving remainders.

    a $7 \overline{)6542}$ b $4 \overline{)2937}$

    c $6 \overline{)8605}$ d $8 \overline{)3262}$

39 Rewrite each of these answers, giving the remainder as a fraction.

    a $5025 \div 4 = 1256$ r1 _____

    b $9573 \div 7 = 1367$ r4 _____

40 Solve these problems.

    a A school has £**58** to buy netballs. Each ball costs £**6**.
       How many balls can the school buy? _____

    b I have **61** cakes. Each box holds **8** cakes.
       How many boxes do I need to hold all the cakes? _____

For help with the questions on this page see
Understanding Maths: Multiplication & Division **pages 39–44.**

Multiplication & Division

41 Use the grid method to do these.

a 6 × 186 = _____

× | | |

b 7 × 247 = _____

× | | |

c 5 × 683 = _____

× | | |

d 8 × 974 = _____

× | | |

e 6512 × 6 = _____

× | | | |

f 4876 × 9 = _____

× | | | |

42 Multiply these numbers using any method you choose. Use spare paper for working.

a 19 × 631 = _____ **b** 36 × 263 = _____ **c** 42 × 537 = _____

d 429 × 54 = _____ **e** 578 × 48 = _____ **f** 689 × 56 = _____

g 5739 × 25 = _____ **h** 8334 × 38 = _____ **i** 9053 × 87 = _____

43 Answer these division questions, using short division, giving remainders as decimals.

a 8) 3 9 0 8

b 4) 2 6 3 3

c 8) 8 7 6 6

d 5) 4 2 3 3

44 Answer these division questions, using long division, with remainders.

a 12) 5 0 3 2

b 11) 4 9 3 7

For help with the questions on this page see
Understanding Maths: Multiplication & Division pages 45–50.

45 Answer these questions.

    a $3.6 \times 10 =$ _____   **b** $0.78 \times 100 =$ _____

    c $56.7 \times 100 =$ _____   **d** $42.3 \times 100 =$ _____

    e $32.7 \div 100 =$ _____   **f** $4.6 \div 10 =$ _____

    g $53 \div 100 =$ _____   **h** $70 \div 100 =$ _____

46 Multiply these decimals.

    a $2.6 \times 4 =$ _____   **b** $7.48 \times 6 =$ _____

    c $46.7 \times 2.1 =$ _____   **d** $12.3 \times 5.6 =$ _____

47 Answer these division questions.

    a $3 \overline{)\, 6\ 5\ .\ 4}$ **b** $4 \overline{)\, 5\ .\ 3\ 6}$

48 How much cheaper is it to pay **12** monthly payments of £**181** than paying four payments of £**546**? _____

49 Answer the questions in each pair.

    a $12 + 4 \div 4 - 2 =$ _____   **b** $7 + 3 \times 2 - 1 + 9 =$ _____

    $(12 + 4) \div (4 - 2) =$ _____ $(7 + 3) \times (2 - 1) + 9 =$ _____

For help with the questions on this page see
Understanding Maths: Multiplication & Division pages 51–56.

Fractions

1 What fraction of each shape is shaded? **a**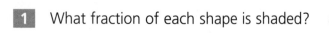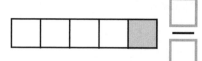

b 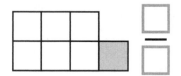 **c** 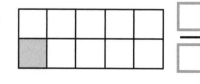 **d**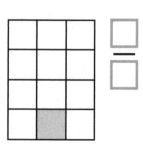

2 Colour these fractions.

a 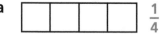 $\frac{1}{4}$ **b**  $\frac{1}{6}$ **c**  $\frac{2}{5}$

3 **Tick** the fractions shaded that are **correctly** named, and **cross** any that are **incorrect**.

a 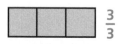 $\frac{3}{3}$ **b**  $\frac{1}{4}$ **c**  $\frac{2}{4}$

d 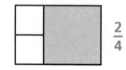 $\frac{2}{4}$ **e** 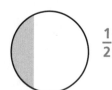 $\frac{1}{2}$ **f** 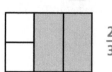 $\frac{2}{3}$

4 Divide the number by the denominator to answer these questions.

a $\frac{1}{3}$ of 24 = _____ **b** $\frac{1}{8}$ of 32 = _____ **c** $\frac{1}{5}$ of 20 = _____ **d** $\frac{1}{6}$ of 12 = _____

5 Answer these questions mentally.

a A man earned **£80**. He gave **one-fifth** to charity. How much did he give?

b **One-quarter** of a class of **32** children is boys. How many are boys?

c There are **40** pages in a book. **One-eighth** of the pages contain pictures. How many pages contain pictures?

d **One-sixth** of the children in a school have packed lunch. There are **120** children in the school. How many have packed lunch?

For help with the questions on this page see
Understanding Maths: Fractions pages 4–7.

6 What fraction of these objects is shaded?

a 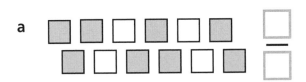 $\dfrac{}{}$

b  $\dfrac{}{}$

7 Count on or back in equal steps to continue the sequences.

a $4\frac{1}{2}$ 5 $5\frac{1}{2}$ 6   ____   ____   ____   ____   ____   ____

b $2\frac{1}{2}$ $2\frac{3}{4}$ 3 $3\frac{1}{4}$ ____   ____   ____   ____   ____   ____

c $10\frac{1}{4}$ 10 $9\frac{3}{4}$ $9\frac{1}{2}$ ____   ____   ____   ____   ____   ____

8 Find:

a $\dfrac{2}{3}$ of **12** ____   b $\dfrac{2}{3}$ of **18** ____   c $\dfrac{3}{4}$ of **16** ____   d $\dfrac{3}{4}$ of **20** ____

9 Find:

a $\dfrac{3}{8}$ of **16** ____   b $\dfrac{3}{8}$ of **24** ____   c $\dfrac{5}{8}$ of **32** ____   d $\dfrac{5}{8}$ of **40** ____

e $\dfrac{3}{4}$ of **40** ____   f $\dfrac{5}{6}$ of **36** ____   g $\dfrac{7}{9}$ of **27** ____   h $\dfrac{7}{10}$ of **80** ____

10 Count on in tenths.

a $\frac{3}{10}$, $\frac{4}{10}$, $\frac{}{10}$, $\frac{}{10}$, $\frac{7}{10}$, $\frac{}{10}$, $\frac{9}{10}$, $\frac{10}{10}$, $\frac{11}{10}$, $\frac{12}{10}$, $\frac{}{10}$, $\frac{}{10}$, $\frac{15}{10}$ ...

b $\frac{7}{10}$, $\frac{8}{10}$, $\frac{9}{10}$, **1**, **1**$\frac{1}{10}$, **1**$\frac{2}{10}$, , , **1**$\frac{5}{10}$, ...

11 Divide each number by **10** and write your answers as fractions with the denominator **10**.

a $7 \div 10 =$ _____   b $9 \div 10 =$ _____   c $11 \div 10 =$ _____

For help with the questions on this page see
Understanding Maths: Fractions pages 7–13.

12 Add these fractions and give your answers as improper (top-heavy) fractions.

a $\frac{6}{10} + \frac{5}{10} = $ _____

b $\frac{4}{9} + \frac{7}{9} = $ _____

c $\frac{5}{6} + \frac{2}{6} = $ _____

d $\frac{7}{8} + \frac{6}{8} = $ _____

13 Add these fractions and give your answers as mixed numbers.

a $\frac{3}{4} + \frac{3}{4} = $ _____

b $\frac{4}{7} + \frac{6}{7} = $ _____

c $\frac{7}{10} + \frac{8}{10} + \frac{8}{10} = $ _____

d $\frac{5}{6} + \frac{4}{6} + \frac{2}{6} = $ _____

14 Subtract these fractions, giving your answers as mixed numbers.

a $\frac{8}{4} - \frac{1}{4} = $ _____

b $\frac{18}{5} - \frac{4}{5} = $ _____

c $\frac{19}{10} - \frac{6}{10} = $ _____

d $\frac{20}{7} - \frac{3}{7} = $ _____

15 Compare these fractions, writing < or > between them.

a $\frac{1}{4}$ _____ $\frac{1}{6}$

b $\frac{1}{8}$ _____ $\frac{1}{2}$

c $\frac{1}{9}$ _____ $\frac{1}{10}$

d $\frac{1}{9}$ _____ $\frac{1}{3}$

e $\frac{1}{3}$ _____ $\frac{1}{10}$

f $\frac{1}{2}$ _____ $\frac{1}{3}$

16 Order these fractions, starting with the largest.

a $\frac{3}{5}$ $\frac{1}{3}$ $\frac{3}{4}$ $\frac{6}{7}$ $\frac{1}{2}$ _____

b $\frac{1}{5}$ $\frac{4}{5}$ $\frac{9}{10}$ $\frac{3}{5}$ $\frac{1}{4}$ $\frac{7}{10}$ _____

For help with the questions on this page see
Understanding Maths: Fractions pages 15–18.

Fractions

17 Write a fraction that is equivalent to:

a $\frac{1}{2}$ _____

b $\frac{1}{5}$ _____

c $\frac{2}{3}$ _____

18 Compare these fractions, writing <, > or = between them.

a $\frac{2}{3}$ _____ $\frac{1}{6}$

b $\frac{2}{5}$ _____ $\frac{2}{6}$

c $\frac{2}{6}$ _____ $\frac{1}{3}$

d $\frac{2}{8}$ _____ $\frac{1}{5}$

e $\frac{6}{12}$ _____ $\frac{3}{4}$

f $\frac{6}{8}$ _____ $\frac{3}{4}$

19 Count on in hundredths.

a $\frac{3}{100}$, $\frac{4}{100}$, $\frac{\quad}{100}$, $\frac{\quad}{100}$, $\frac{\quad}{100}$, $\frac{\quad}{100}$, $\frac{\quad}{100}$, $\frac{10}{100}$, $\frac{11}{100}$, $\frac{\quad}{100}$, $\frac{\quad}{100}$ ...

b $1\frac{99}{100}$, 2, $2\frac{1}{100}$, ☐, ☐, $2\frac{4}{100}$, ☐, ☐, ☐, ☐, ☐ ...

20 Write your answers as fractions with the denominator **100**.

a $9 \div 100 =$ _____

b $45 \div 100 =$ _____

c $80 \div 100 =$ _____

21 Simplify the fraction first to help you answer the question in your head.

a $\boxed{\frac{3}{12}}$ of **20** = $\frac{\boxed{}}{\boxed{}}$ of **20** = _____

b $\boxed{\frac{5}{10}}$ of **22** = $\frac{\boxed{}}{\boxed{}}$ of **22** = _____

c $\boxed{\frac{6}{10}}$ of **25** = $\frac{\boxed{}}{\boxed{}}$ of **25** = _____

d $\boxed{\frac{70}{100}}$ of **120** = $\frac{\boxed{}}{\boxed{}}$ of **120** = _____

For help with the questions on this page see
Understanding Maths: Fractions **pages 19–23.**

Fractions

22 Join each fraction to its correct position on the line.

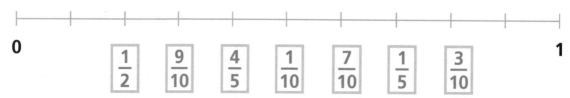

0   1

$\frac{1}{2}$ $\frac{9}{10}$ $\frac{4}{5}$ $\frac{1}{10}$ $\frac{7}{10}$ $\frac{1}{5}$ $\frac{3}{10}$

23 Write the fractions the arrows are pointing to. Think about equivalent fractions!

a

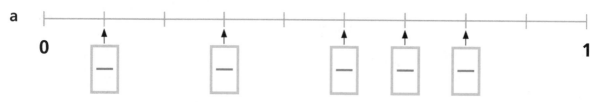

b

24 Choose which number to divide the numerator and denominator of the fraction by to simplify each fraction to its simplest form. The number must be a factor of both numbers.

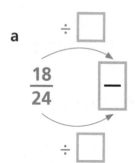

a $\frac{18}{24}$

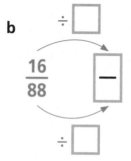

b $\frac{16}{88}$

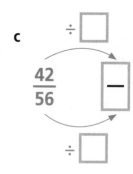

c $\frac{42}{56}$

25 Change these improper fractions to mixed numbers.

a $\frac{9}{2}$ _____   **b** $\frac{7}{3}$ _____   **c** $\frac{8}{5}$ _____   **d** $\frac{11}{4}$ _____

e $\frac{21}{10}$ _____   **f** $\frac{13}{8}$ _____   **g** $\frac{19}{6}$ _____   **h** $\frac{27}{4}$ _____

i $\frac{22}{7}$ _____   **j** $\frac{28}{8}$ _____   **k** $\frac{43}{9}$ _____   **l** $\frac{57}{10}$ _____

For help with the questions on this page see
***Understanding Maths: Fractions* pages 24–28.**

26 Change these mixed numbers to improper fractions.

a $5\frac{4}{9}$ _____   b $6\frac{3}{4}$ _____   c $7\frac{3}{7}$ _____   d $8\frac{4}{5}$ _____

e $9\frac{2}{9}$ _____   f $11\frac{7}{10}$ _____   g $12\frac{7}{8}$ _____   h $15\frac{2}{7}$ _____

27 How many pairs of equivalent fractions can you find?

| $\frac{35}{9}$ | $6\frac{5}{9}$ | $\frac{51}{9}$ | $5\frac{6}{9}$ | $\frac{36}{9}$ | $3\frac{8}{9}$ | $\frac{59}{9}$ |

28 Change these fractions to their simplest form.

a $\frac{15}{45}$ _____   b $\frac{16}{32}$ _____   c $\frac{21}{63}$ _____   d $\frac{8}{56}$ _____

29 Answer these questions by first changing one fraction to an equivalent one so that they have a common denominator.

a $\frac{2}{9} + \frac{2}{3} =$ _____   b $\frac{1}{4} + \frac{5}{8} =$ _____

30 Answer these questions, giving your answers as mixed numbers and simplifying if possible.

a $\frac{5}{6} \times 3 =$ _____   b $4 \times \frac{11}{12} =$ _____

31 Change these fractions so they have a common denominator. Circle the larger fraction in each pair.

a $\frac{4}{5}$ or $\frac{7}{10}$ b $\frac{3}{4}$ or $\frac{7}{8}$ c $\frac{3}{8}$ or $\frac{7}{16}$

d $\frac{2}{5}$ or $\frac{3}{10}$ e $\frac{3}{4}$ or $\frac{4}{5}$ f $\frac{5}{6}$ or $\frac{7}{9}$

g $\frac{1}{3}$ or $\frac{2}{9}$ h $\frac{5}{7}$ or $\frac{2}{3}$ i $\frac{6}{7}$ or $\frac{19}{21}$

32 Circle the largest fraction in each set.

a $\frac{2}{3}$ $\frac{7}{9}$ $\frac{13}{18}$ b $\frac{3}{4}$ $\frac{13}{16}$ $\frac{5}{8}$ c $\frac{7}{12}$ $\frac{5}{6}$ $\frac{19}{24}$

For help with the questions on this page see
Understanding Maths: Fractions pages 27–32.

Fractions

33 Put these fractions in order, smallest first, using common denominators.

a $\frac{2}{3}$ $\frac{1}{3}$ $\frac{5}{9}$ _____ _____ _____

b $\frac{3}{8}$ $\frac{5}{8}$ $\frac{1}{4}$ _____ _____ _____

c $\frac{1}{6}$ $\frac{1}{4}$ $\frac{1}{3}$ _____ _____ _____

d $\frac{4}{5}$ $\frac{9}{10}$ $\frac{19}{20}$ _____ _____ _____

34 Answer these questions. Change the fractions to have a common denominator.

a $1\frac{5}{9} + 1\frac{1}{3} =$ _____

b $4\frac{3}{4} + 3\frac{1}{8} =$ _____

c $3\frac{2}{3} + \frac{2}{5} =$ _____

d $\frac{5}{12} + 2\frac{2}{3} =$ _____

35 Answer these, where the fractions in each question have the same denominator, but the second fraction is larger.

a $7\frac{1}{9} - 2\frac{3}{9} =$ _____

b $9\frac{1}{10} - 1\frac{5}{10} =$ _____

c $8\frac{2}{7} - 4\frac{4}{7} =$ _____

d $7\frac{2}{5} - 5\frac{3}{5} =$ _____

36 Answer these questions and simplify your answers.

a $\frac{2}{5} \div 3 =$ _____

b $\frac{4}{7} \div 2 =$ _____

37 Answer these questions, giving answers in the simplest form.

a $\frac{2}{5} \times \frac{3}{4} =$ _____

b $\frac{5}{8} \times \frac{4}{10} =$ _____

c $\frac{4}{5} \times \frac{3}{4} =$ _____

d $\frac{5}{7} \times \frac{3}{4} =$ _____

For help with the questions on this page see
Understanding Maths: Fractions pages 34–40.

Decimals & Percentages

1 Draw a ring around the **tenths** digit in these numbers.

a 3.5
b 4.7
c 2.9

d 16.4
e 53.2
f 36.8

g 9.32
h 7.19
i 26.76

2 Draw a ring around the **hundredths** digit in these numbers.

a 6.37
b 5.82
c 9.79

d 17.32
e 45.21
f 128.08

g 5.569
h 8.307
i 15.792

3 What is the **red** digit worth in each of these numbers?

a **4.57** _____
b **17.52** _____
c **38.17** _____

d **216.66** _____
e **250.95** _____
f **96.831** _____

4 Write each fraction as a decimal.

a $\frac{9}{10}$ _____
b $\frac{4}{10}$ _____

c $\frac{43}{100}$ _____
d $\frac{25}{100}$ _____

5 Divide each number and write the answer as a decimal.

a $13 \div 10 =$ _____
b $732 \div 10 =$ _____

c $43 \div 10 =$ _____
d $8 \div 100 =$ _____

e $503 \div 10 =$ _____
f $261 \div 100 =$ _____

For help with the questions on this page see
Understanding Maths: Decimals and Percentages **pages 4–7.**

Decimals & Percentages

6 Mark these numbers on the number lines, using arrows.

a **1.3, 1.8, 0.5, 0.1**

b **1.9, 2.7, 0.4, 1.6**

c **3.2, 4.5, 4.3, 5.8**

7 Round these numbers to the nearest **whole number**.

a **2.6** → ☐   b **4.1** → ☐   c **5.9** → ☐

d **7.7** → ☐   e **11.5** → ☐   f **8.5** → ☐

8 Compare the decimals in each pair. Write < or > between them.

a **0.1** ____ **0.7**   b **0.09** ____ **0.02**

c **0.08** ____ **0.03**   d **0.6** ____ **0.9**

e **0.13** ____ **0.09**   f **5.04** ____ **4.04**

g **0.68** ____ **0.86**   h **5.7** ____ **7.5**

9 Write the numbers in the bags to make the scales tilt correctly.

a **3.2kg, 2.9kg**   b **4.65kg, 4.56kg**   c **6.78kg, 6.87kg**

10 Put these decimals in order, starting with the smallest.

a **0.9, 0.5, 0.8, 0.2** _____

b **0.07, 0.03, 0.06, 0.08** _____

For help with the questions on this page see
Understanding Maths: Decimals & Percentages **pages 8–11.**

Decimals & Percentages

11 Write the decimal each arrow is pointing to.

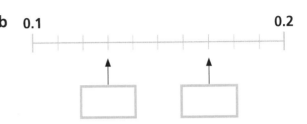

12 Round these numbers to the nearest **whole number**.

a 12.17 → ☐   b 19.49 → ☐   c 20.01 → ☐

13 Draw a ring around the larger number in each pair.

a 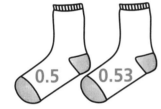   b 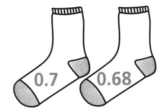   c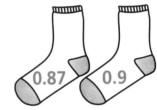

d    e 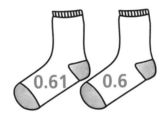   f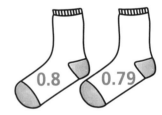

14 Put these decimals in order of size, smallest first.

a 0.7, 0.6, 0.65, 0.36 _____

b 0.8, 0.85, 0.93, 0.9 _____

c 0.48, 0.51, 0.5, 0.49 _____

d 1.56, 1.6, 1.5, 1.57 _____

e 2.45, 2.54, 2.35, 2.53 _____

15 Write these in order of size, largest first.

a **0.34**kg, **0.52**kg, **0.40**kg, **0.5**kg   ☐ ☐ ☐ ☐

b **7.9**m, **6.5**m, **8.0**m, **7.6**m   ☐ ☐ ☐ ☐

For help with the questions on this page see
Understanding Maths: Decimals & Percentages **pages 13–17.**

16 Write these decimals as fractions in their simplest form.

a 0.75    b 0.6   c 0.7   d 0.5

17 Add these numbers.

a		b		c		d		e	
	2 3 . 7		3 4 . 7		4 2 . 8		5 4 . 6 2		3 4 . 0 9
+	1 7 . 1	+	2 8 . 4	+	2 7 . 2	+	3 5 . 0 3	+	8 3 . 8 7

18 Subtract these numbers.

a		b		c		d		e	
	5 8 . 7		3 7 . 5		8 4 . 8		6 4 . 8 2		7 2 . 3 1
−	1 6 . 1	−	2 3 . 9	−	3 9 . 3	−	4 5 . 1 7	−	6 4 . 5 8

19 Solve these problems.

a Gita has a piece of ribbon that is **8.6**m long. She cuts off a length that is **3.8**m long. How much ribbon is left? _____

b What is the total length of a line that is **0.7**cm longer than **5.6**cm? _____

20 Colour the box that shows the value of the underlined digit.

8.64<u>2</u> | 20 | | 2.0 | | 0.2 | | 0.02 | | 0.002 |

21 Put these decimals in order of size, smallest first.

a 0.3, 0.35, 0.174, 0.53, 0.573 _____

b 8.73, 8.238, 8.391, 8.8, 8.368 _____

22 Write these in order of size, largest first.

a £**5.02**, £**5**, £**5.20**, **550**p, £**5.05** _____

b **7.653**g, **6.75**g, **6.57**g, **5.762**g, **5.72**g _____

For help with the questions on this page see
Understanding Maths: Decimals & Percentages pages 18–24.

23 Solve these measurement problems.

a A length of road is **3.352**km long. Georgia runs from one end to the other. She stops after **1.369**km. How far does she have still to run? _____

b Rebecca's baby boy weighed **3.107**kg at birth. He now weighs **4.5**kg. By how much has his weight increased? _____

24 Complete these clothing labels, making sure they total **100**%.

a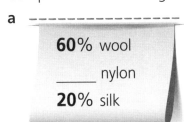

60% wool

_____ nylon

20% silk

b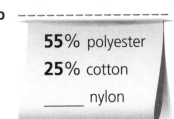

55% polyester

25% cotton

_____ nylon

c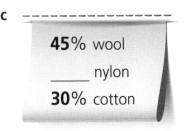

45% wool

_____ nylon

30% cotton

25 What is **50**% of:

a 16 → _____   **b** 28 → _____   **c** 40 → _____

d 96 → _____   **e** 250 → _____   **f** 400 → _____

26 What is **25**% of:

a 12 → _____   **b** 20 → _____   **c** 40 → _____

d 80 → _____   **e** 140 → _____   **f** 500 → _____

27 What is **75**% of:

a 8 → _____   **b** 16 → _____   **c** 36 → _____

d 76 → _____   **e** 200 → _____   **f** 6000 → _____

28 Find **10**% of:

a £130 → _____   **b** 350g → _____   **c** 2580m → _____

29 Find **30**% of:

a £30 → _____   **b** 150g → _____   **c** 800m → _____

30 Find **45**% of:

a £80 → _____   **b** 200km → _____   **c** 500cm → _____

For help with the questions on this page see
***Understanding Maths: Decimals & Percentages* pages 25–30.**

Decimals & Percentages

31 Use the number lines to help you to complete the tables.

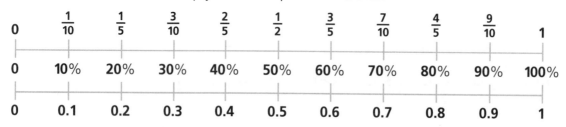

Percentage	Decimal	Fraction
30%		
70%		
	0.2	
		$\frac{8}{10}$

Percentage	Decimal	Fraction
	0.6	
40%		
		1
	0.1	

32 Change these percentages into decimals.

a 42% → ☐   b 35% → ☐   c 63% → ☐

d 3% → ☐   e 99% → ☐   f 100% → ☐

33 Change these decimals into percentages.

a 0.46 → ☐   b 0.87 → ☐   c 0.91 → ☐

d 0.7 → ☐   e 0.8 → ☐   f 0.01 → ☐

34 Solve these problems.

a The school hockey team played **25** games. They won **60**% of them.
How many games did they win? _____

b A school party of **90** children go the London Eye. **40**% of them are girls.
How many are girls? _____

35 Use a calculator to find these percentages.

a **39**% of £**150** = _____   b **48**% of £**64** = _____

c **26**% of £**82** = _____   d **78**% of **160**kg = _____

e **67**% of **262**kg = _____   f **29**% of **348**kg = _____

For help with the questions on this page see
Understanding Maths: Decimals & Percentages pages 31–34.

Decimals & Percentages

36 Write each answer as a decimal.

   a $0.08 \times 10 =$ _____

   b $0.004 \times 10 =$ _____

   c $0.03 \times 100 =$ _____

   d $0.017 \times 100 =$ _____

   e $0.008 \times 1000 =$ _____

   f $0.036 \times 1000 =$ _____

37 Convert each fraction to a decimal and then to a percentage.

   a $\frac{1}{8} =$ _____ _____

   b $\frac{3}{8} =$ _____ _____

38 Answer these questions mentally.

   a $0.4 \times 8 =$ _____

   b $0.07 \times 5 =$ _____

   c $0.9 \times 5 =$ _____

   d $0.06 \times 3 =$ _____

   e $0.9 \times 0.7 =$ _____

   f $0.08 \times 0.8 =$ _____

   g $0.5 \times 0.8 =$ _____

   h $0.05 \times 0.4 =$ _____

39 Answer these questions mentally.

   a $0.24 \div 3 =$ _____

   b $3.6 \div 3 =$ _____

   c $3.6 \div 4 =$ _____

   d $0.2 \div 5 =$ _____

40 Round each of these recurring decimals to two decimal places.

   a $0.6666666 \ldots$ _____

   b $0.88888888 \ldots$ _____

   c $0.2727272 \ldots$ _____

   d $0.37373737 \ldots$ _____

   e $0.1111111 \ldots$ _____

   f $0.526526526 \ldots$ _____

For help with the questions on this page see
Understanding Maths: Decimals & Percentages **pages 36–40.**

Number Patterns & Algebra

1 Fill in the missing numbers in these sequences.

a [ ] [ ] [ ] [ ] [ ] [152] [162] [172] [ ] [ ]

b [ ] [ ] [ ] [183] [ ] [ ] [ ] [143] [ ] [ ]

c [ ] [ ] [452] [ ] [ ] [ ] [ ] [412] [ ] [ ] [ ]

2 Count on in hundreds starting from:

a 704 _____ _____ _____ _____ _____ _____ _____ _____ _____

b 1942 _____ _____ _____ _____ _____ _____ _____ _____ _____

3 Count back in hundreds starting from:

a 4279 _____ _____ _____ _____ _____ _____ _____ _____ _____

b 9302 _____ _____ _____ _____ _____ _____ _____ _____ _____

4 Fill in the missing numbers in these sequences.

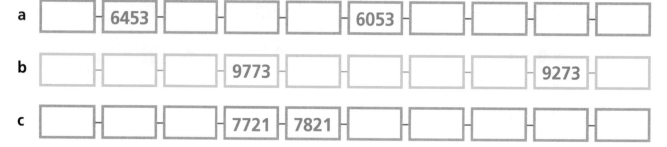

a [ ] [6453] [ ] [ ] [ ] [6053] [ ] [ ] [ ] [ ]

b [ ] [ ] [ ] [9773] [ ] [ ] [ ] [9273] [ ]

c [ ] [ ] [ ] [7721] [7821] [ ] [ ] [ ] [ ] [ ]

5 Count on in threes from:

12 _____ _____ _____ _____ _____ _____ _____ _____

6 Count back in fours from:

48 _____ _____ _____ _____ _____ _____ _____ _____

7 Count back in fives from:

55 _____ _____ _____ _____ _____ _____ _____ _____

For help with the questions on this page see
Understanding Maths: Number Patterns & Algebra **pages 5–7.**

Number Patterns & Algebra

8 Draw a ring around the numbers that are:

a
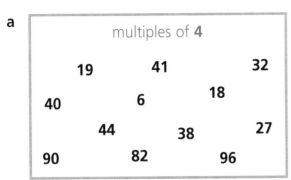

multiples of **4**

19   41   32
40   6   18
44   38   27
90   82   96

b
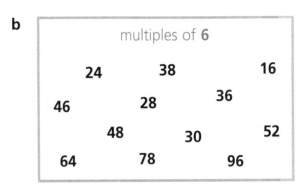

multiples of **6**

24   38   16
46   28   36
48   30   52
64   78   96

9 Use the key to draw the correct shapes around the numbers.

20   52   40
    90   60   62

45   34   81   30   240

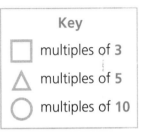

Key
☐ multiples of 3
△ multiples of 5
○ multiples of 10

10 Continue each sequence.

a Add **25**
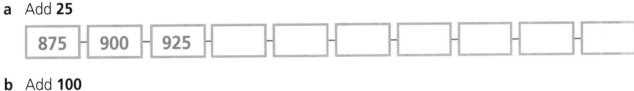

| 875 | 900 | 925 | | | | | | | |

b Add **100**

| 3600 | 3700 | 3800 | | | | | | | |

c Add _____

| 1350 | 1400 | 1450 | | | | | | | |

11 Fill in the missing numbers in these sequences.

a 77, 70, _____, 56, _____, 42, _____, _____, 21 …

b 36, _____, 48, _____, 60, _____, 72 …

c 108, _____, 90, _____, 72, _____, 54, 45, _____, 27 …

For help with the questions on this page see
***Understanding Maths: Number Patterns & Algebra* pages 8–12.**

Number Patterns & Algebra

12 Draw a ring around the numbers that are:

a

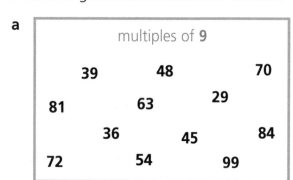

multiples of **9**

39 48 70
81 63 29
36 45 84
72 54 99

b

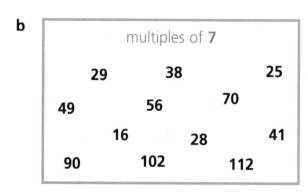

multiples of **7**

29 38 25
49 56 70
16 28 41
90 102 112

13 Fill in the missing numbers in these sequences.

a 27 ____ ____ ____ ____ 62   **b** 15 ____ ____ ____ ____ 55

c 136 ____ ____ ____ ____ 91   **d** 237 ____ ____ ____ ____ 172

14 Fill in the missing numbers in these sequences.

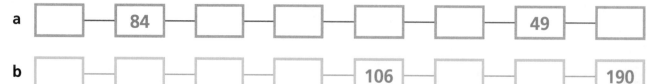

a [ ]—[84]—[ ]—[ ]—[ ]—[ ]—[49]—[ ]

b [ ]—[ ]—[ ]—[ ]—[106]—[ ]—[ ]—[190]

15 Continue each sequence and then explain it.

a

[1]—[4]—[9]—[16]—[ ]—[ ]
a _____
_____

b

[21]—[34]—[47]—[ ]—[ ]—[ ]
b _____
_____

c

[15]—[9]—[3]—[ ]—[ ]—[ ]
c _____
_____

16 Continue each sequence and then explain it.

a

[9]—[$8\frac{2}{3}$]—[$8\frac{1}{3}$]—[ ]—[ ]—[ ]
a _____
_____

b
[$3\frac{3}{4}$]—[4]—[$4\frac{1}{4}$]—[ ]—[ ]—[ ]
b _____
_____

For help with the questions on this page see
Understanding Maths: Number Patterns & Algebra pages 12–15.

Number Patterns & Algebra

17 Fill in the missing numbers.

  a 0.02, 0.03, _____ , 0.05, 0.06, 0.07, 0.08, _____ , 0.1, 0.11, _____ ...

  b 0.88, 0.89, _____ , 0.91, _____ , 0.93, 0.94, 0.95, 0.96, 0.97, 0.98, 0.99, _____ , 1.01 ...

18 Complete these sequences.

  a

  b

19 Continue these sequences.

  a −14 −12 −10 −8 ____ ____ ____ ____ ____ ____ ____

  b −15 −13 −11 −9 ____ ____ ____ ____ ____ ____ ____

20 Fill in the gaps in these sequences.

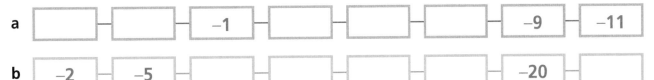

21 Find the difference between each pair of temperatures.

  a −1°C and 4°C _____   **b** −9°C and −3°C _____

  c 7°C and −9°C _____   **d** −21°C and −5°C _____

22 Put these temperatures in order, starting with the coldest.

  a −1°C 1°C −5°C −3°C 5°C _____

  b 9°C −4°C −10°C 0°C −1°C _____

23 Find the lengths of the sides of these squares.

  a 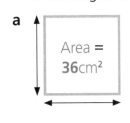   **b** 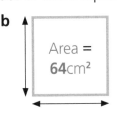   **c** 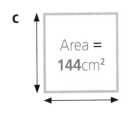   **d**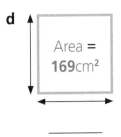

_____   _____   _____   _____

> **For help with the questions on this page see**
> *Understanding Maths: Number Patterns & Algebra pages 16–22.*

Number Patterns & Algebra

24 Work out the value of each of these.

    a XVI _____   **b** LXII _____   **c** XXIV _____   **d** LXXIII _____

25 Write each of these in Roman numerals.

    a 37 _____   **b** 68 _____   **c** 40 _____   **d** 81 _____

26 Write the missing values.

    a $3^3 =$ _____   **b** _____ $^3 = 8$ **c** _____ $^3 = 1000$ **d** $5^3 =$ _____

27 Write the lengths of the sides of these rectangles. Use your answers to help write all the factors of **48**.

a

4cm   Area = **48**cm²   _____ cm

_____ cm

b

_____ cm   Area = **48**cm²

24cm

c

6cm   Area = **48**cm²

_____ cm

d

3cm   Area = **48**cm²

_____ cm

factors of **48** _____

28 Write the lengths of the sides of these rectangles. Use your answers to help you write all the factors of **72**.

a

3cm   Area = **72**cm²

_____ cm

b

_____ cm   Area = **72**cm²

_____ cm

c

_____ cm   Area = **72**cm²

_____ cm

d

_____ cm   Area = **72**cm²

_____ cm

e

_____ cm   Area = **72**cm²

_____ cm

factors of **72** _____

For help with the questions on this page see
Understanding Maths: Number Patterns & Algebra pages 23–26.

Number Patterns & Algebra

29 Find all the factors of:

24	60	64	120
1 24			

30 Write the factors of each of the numbers in question 29 in a list. Start with the smallest.

a The factors of **24** are _____

b The factors of **60** are _____

c The factors of **64** are _____

d The factors of **120** are _____

31 Find the common factors other than **1** of each pair of numbers.

a **12** and **28** _____ and _____

b **30** and **40** _____ , _____ and _____

32 Write all the common factors other than **1** of each set of numbers.

a **12**, **18** and **30** _____

b **28**, **42** and **56** _____

c **15**, **30** and **60** _____

33 List all the prime numbers up to **100**.

_____

_____

For help with the questions on this page see
Understanding Maths: Number Patterns & Algebra **pages 27–31.**

Number Patterns & Algebra

34 Write these numbers as products of their prime factors. The first has been done for you.

a 8 ___2 × 2 × 2___   **b** 16 _____   **c** 24 _____

d 32 _____   **e** 36 _____   **f** 40 _____

g 60 _____   **h** 27 _____   **i** 96 _____

35 Write the first ten multiples of **3** and **7**. Draw a ring around any common multiples.

a 3 _____

b 7 _____

36 Write the first 10 multiples of **6** and **9**. Draw a ring around any common multiples.

a 6 _____

b 9 _____

37 Write the smallest common multiple of:

a **5** and **8** _____   **b** **3** and **6** _____   **c** **3, 4** and **8** _____

38 These questions are all similar. Write a formula to show how you could solve them.

a

*How many days are there in **3** weeks?*

*How many days are there in **9** weeks?*

*How many days are there in **156** weeks?*

_____

b

*How many weeks are there in **6** years?*

*How many weeks are there in **8** years?*

*How many weeks are there in **25** years?*

_____

c

*Chews cost **5p** each. How much will **8** chews cost?*

*Chews cost **5p** each. How much will **15** chews cost?*

*Chews cost **5p** each. How much will **23** chews cost?*

_____

> **For help with the questions on this page see**
> *Understanding Maths: Number Patterns & Algebra* **pages 32–36.**

39 Join each situation to its formula.

a
| Buster ate **c** dog biscuits. Digger ate twice as many. How many did Digger eat? |

c + 4

b
| Harry has **9** pounds. He loses **c** pounds. How much does he have now? |

2c

c
| Ben spends £**c** on burgers and £**4** on chocolate. How much does he spend? |

10 + c

d
| Erik earns £**10** in the morning and £**c** in the afternoon. How much does he earn in total? |

9 – c

40 Write the term-to-term rule for each sequence.

a 6, 9, 12, 15, 18, 21, …

Start at _____ . Each term _____

b 98, 93, 88, 83, 78, 73, …

Start at _____ . Each term _____

c 1, 5, 9, 13, 17, 21, 25, …

Start at _____ . Each term _____

41 Fill in the table to write the first 10 terms of the sequence **6n**.

n =	1	2	3	4	5	6	7	8	9	10
6n =										

42 Fill in the table to write the first 10 terms of the sequence **2n – 1**.

n =	1	2	3	4	5	6	7	8	9	10
2n – 1	1									

> **For help with the questions on this page see**
> *Understanding Maths: Number Patterns & Algebra* **pages 37–40.**

Problem Solving

1 Write the number fact for each of these stories.

a I had £**13** and was given £**5** by my mum, leaving me with £**18**. _____

b The cook had **20** potatoes. He shared them out between
four of us. We each got five potatoes. _____

c Six horses in the field each have four legs. This is **24** legs altogether. _____

2 Answer these number story questions.

a A stool has three legs. How many legs do seven stools have? _____

b Six frogs were on a stone. Four more jumped on.
How many were there then? _____

c My dad made eight cakes. He shared them out
between four people. How many did they each get? _____

3 Fill in the missing operation sign to make these number facts correct.

a 25 ☐ 2 = 50   b 40 ☐ 8 = 48   c 100 ☐ 2 = 50

d 34 ☐ 16 = 50   e 36 ☐ 5 = 31   f 32 ☐ 4 = 128

g 45 ☐ 55 = 100   h 48 ☐ 8 = 6   i 34 ☐ 17 = 17

4 What is the inverse operation for:

a subtraction? _____   b division? _____

c multiplication? _____   d addition? _____

5 Work out the missing number by rearranging the question.

a 47 − ☐ = 16   b 18 ÷ ☐ = 9   c 18 + ☐ = 42

☐ ☐ ☐ = ☐   ☐ ☐ ☐ = ☐   ☐ ☐ ☐ = ☐

d 8 × ☐ = 56   e 63 − ☐ = 24   f 54 ÷ ☐ = 6

☐ ☐ ☐ = ☐   ☐ ☐ ☐ = ☐   ☐ ☐ ☐ = ☐

For help with the questions on this page see
***Understanding Maths: Problem Solving* pages 4–8.**

Problem Solving

6 Solve these one-step word problems.

 a My book has **48** pages. I have read half the book already.
    How many pages have I left to read? _____

 b A teacher has **23** grey pencils and **19** coloured pencils.
    How many pencils does he have in total? _____

 c My mum is four times older than me. She is **40**. How old am I? _____

7 Solve these two-step word problems.

 a My book has **48** pages. I have read five pages already.
    How many pages must I read to reach the middle of the book? _____

 b **38** cars are in the car park. **9** leave but **17** more arrive.
    How many cars are there now? _____

 c My mum is four times older than me. She is **36**.
    How old will I be in five years' time? _____

8 Solve these problems.

 a There were **3324** men, **2110** women and **1203** children
    at a football match. How many people were there altogether? _____

 b In **1999** Kim was **53** years old. In which year was she born? _____

 c In **2011** James was **39** years old. In which year was he born? _____

9 Find the total of all the numbers from:

 a **13** to **21**   ☐   **b** **26** to **34**   ☐
    (find pairs that make 34)   (find pairs that make 60)

   13 14 15 16 ⑰ 18 19 20 21   26 27 28 29 ㉚ 31 32 33 34
              ⌄34⌄   ⌄60⌄

 c **11** to **29** (find pairs that make 40)   ☐

   11 12 13 14 15 16 17 18 19 ⑳ 21 22 23 24 25 26 27 28 29
                         ⌄40⌄

 d **11** to **34** (find pairs that make 45 – there is no middle number this time)   ☐

11 12 13 14 15 16 17 18 19 20 21 22 23 24 25 26 27 28 29 30 31 32 33 34
                      ⌄45⌄
                    ⌄45⌄

For help with the questions on this page see
Understanding Maths: Problem Solving pages 9–14.

10 Four letters S, T, U and V are arranged next to each other. Finish this list to show all the possible orders in which they could be written. Notice how they are arranged systematically.

S	T	U	V		T	S	U	V		U	S	T	V		V	S	__	__
S	T	V	U		T	S	V	U		U	S	__	__		__	__	__	__

S	U	T	V		T	U	S	V		U	T	S	V		V	T	__	__
S	U	V	T		T	U	V	S		U	T	__	__		__	__	__	__

S	V	T	U		T	V	S	U		U	V	S	T		V	U	__	__
S	V	U	T		T	V	__	__		__	__	__	__		__	__	__	__

11 Write all six possible orders of writing the letters A, B, C. Be systematic.

_____   _____   _____   _____   _____   _____

12 Three **odd** numbers are added to make **11**. Find all the different sets of odd numbers with a total of **11**. Be systematic.

1 + 1 + _____

1 + _____ + _____

13 Complete the table to show how many tops you can make with three neck shapes and three colours.

	V-neck top	Round neck top	Collared top
White T-shirt	white V-neck top		
Blue T-shirt			
Black T-shirt			

14 A sweet shop has a special offer. For every five sweets you buy, they give you four sweets for free. Complete the lines of multiples.

Number of sweets you buy:	5	10	____	____	____	____	____
Number of sweets you get free:	4	8	____	____	____	____	____

How many free sweets will you get if you buy **35** sweets? _____

For help with the questions on this page see
Understanding Maths: Problem Solving pages 15–17.

Problem Solving

15 How many cubes will **Shape 10** be made from?

| **Shape 1** | **Shape 2** | **Shape 3** | **Shape 4** | ...**Shape 10?** |

      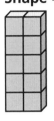

4 cubes   6 cubes   _____ cubes   _____ cubes   _____ cubes

16 How many dots will **Pattern 10** be made from?

Pattern 1   **Pattern 2**   **Pattern 3**   **Pattern 4**   ...**Pattern 10?**

_____ dots   _____ dots   _____ dots   _____ dots   _____ dots

17 Make up a shape from dots to show the **10**th shape.

18 Complete this table to show the results of the problem.
You have a pair of dice. When both dice are rolled and their dots added together, a total is found. In how many different ways can the totals 1 to 12 be found?

Total	1	2	3	4	5	6	7	8	9	10	11	12
Ways	0	1										

For help with the questions on this page see
Understanding Maths: Problem Solving **pages 18–20.**

Problem Solving

19 **a** Count the number of cubes in each shape.
Record the results in the table.

Shape	Cubes

Shape 1   **Shape 2**   **Shape 3**   **Shape 4**

b How many cubes will **Shape 10** be made from? _____

20 **a** Count the number of dots in each pattern.
Record the results in the table.

Pattern	Dots

Pattern 1   **Pattern 2**   **Pattern 3**   **Pattern 4**

b How many dots will **Pattern 10** be made from? _____

21 Solve these one-step money problems.

a I had **94**p and I spent **25**p. How much do I have left?

b Joe was given £**38** for his birthday and £**45** for Christmas.
How much did he get in total?

c Jack is paid £**50** every month. How much does he
earn in a year (**12** months)?

22 Solve these two-step money problems.

a A drink costs £**1.25**. Mr Simpson buys four drinks for his
children. How much change does he get from £**10**?

b Six apples cost **54**p. How much does it cost to buy five apples?

c Shazia saves £**1.80** of her pocket money each week.
After ten weeks she decides to buy a DVD costing £**10**.
How much money does she have left after that?

d I had **69**p. I was given **40**p more and then I spent **57**p.
How much do I have left?

e Ella buys a pencil costing **39**p and a rubber costing **43**p.
How much less than **90**p is this?

For help with the questions on this page see
Understanding Maths: Problem Solving pages 21–24.

Practice

Problem Solving

23 Solve these money problems, changing the amounts to either pounds or pence.

a I had **£45** and I spent **30**p. How much do I have now? _____

b Three items cost **20**p, **£1.75** and **£7**.
What is the total cost of the three items? _____

c I had **£4.52**. I was given **25**p more and then I spent **£2**.
How much did I have left? _____

d Molly saves **85**p of her pocket money each week.
After ten weeks she decides to buy a CD costing **£7.50**.
How much money does she have left after that? _____

24 Solve these measurement problems.

a A tin of beans weighs **250**g. How much do five tins weigh? _____

b A runner ran **9.5**km every day for a week.
How many kilometres did he run in total? _____

c A television has a mass of **8.4**kg. A radio has a mass of
2.9kg. What is the difference between the two masses? _____

d A runner ran **4500**m every day for **20** days.
How much further than **60**km did he run in total? _____

25 Solve these time problems.

a A TV programme lasting **1** hour **45** minutes starts at **8.35** p.m.
What time does it end? _____

b A TV programme lasting **2** hours **20** minutes starts at **4.55** p.m.
What time does it end? _____

c A tennis match lasting **3** hours **15** minutes ends at **4.45** p.m.
What time did it start? _____

d If the time now is **09:55**, what time will it be in **4** hours
20 minutes? _____

26 Solve these problems.

a Zach's plane is due to take off in **55** hours' time.
It is now Saturday at **8** a.m. When is Zach's flight? _____

b Luke earns **£200** per month. How much does he earn in
four years? _____

For help with the questions on this page see
***Understanding Maths: Problem Solving* pages 24–27.**

Problem Solving

27 Solve these problems.

a **78** photos are put into an album where each page holds five photos. How many pages are needed?

_____

b **78** photos are put into an album where each page holds five photos. How many pages are full?

_____

c Chloe has £**59** to buy some new CDs. Each CD costs £**9**. How many can she buy?

_____

d A school has £**77** to buy footballs. Each ball costs £**6**. How many can they buy?

_____

e I have **892** coins. I put them all into bags. Each bag can hold **80** coins. How many bags do I need?

_____

f **125** children are going on a school trip. Each minibus can carry **11** children. How many minibuses will be needed?

_____

28 Choose whether you think it is best to give each answer with a remainder, with a fraction, as a decimal or by rounding the answer.

a **11** pizzas are equally shared among eight people. How much pizza does each person have?

_____

b **37** children are going to a party by car. If each car can hold up to four children, what is the fewest number of cars needed?

_____

c How many **7**p stamps can I buy with **72**p?

_____

29 Write the new temperature after each change.

a It was **3**°C. The temperature fell by **7**°C.

_____

b It was –**6**°C. The temperature rose by **15**°C.

_____

30 Solve these problems.

a Four children each eat $\frac{4}{5}$ of a quiche. How much quiche is eaten? _____

b Sanjeet has four-fifths of a pizza. He shares it equally with Liam. How much pizza do they have each?

_____

c Two children each eat $\frac{7}{8}$ of a cheesecake. How much cheesecake is eaten?

_____

For help with the questions on this page see
Understanding Maths: Problem Solving pages 29–33.

31 Solve these decimal problems.

   a Grace has a piece of ribbon that is **3.2**m long. She cuts off
a length that is **1.65**m long. How much ribbon is left? _____

   b What is the total length of a line that is **0.08**cm longer
than **5.4**cm? _____

32 The ratio of cows to sheep in a field is **5:4**. How many cows and sheep are there if there
are **63** animals in the field?

_____ cows   and _____ sheep

33 Solve these ratio problems.

   a **£49** is shared between two people in the ratio **2:5**.
How much does each person get? _____ and _____

   b **£360** is shared between two people in the ratio **3:7**.
How much does each person get? _____ and _____

34 A gardener has four rows of leeks with **18** in each row.
How many leeks altogether? _____

35 Find the scale factor and use it to help you find the missing lengths.

a

5cm
6cm
25cm
?cm

b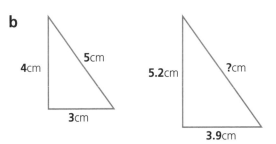

scale factor _____   _____ cm   scale factor _____   _____ cm

36 Solve these problems.

   a How much greater is **80**% of **45** than **75**% of **44**? _____

   b A nurse gives **70**% of a full dose of medicine to a child.
If the full dose is **40**ml, how much is the child given? _____

For help with the questions on this page see
***Understanding Maths: Problem Solving* pages 34–40.**

Geometry & Measurement

1 Complete this table.

Shape	Number of sides	Number of vertices	Straight or curved?
square			
decagon			
rectangle			
circle			
pentagon			
hexagon			
triangle			
octagon			

2 Colour all the **regular** shapes.

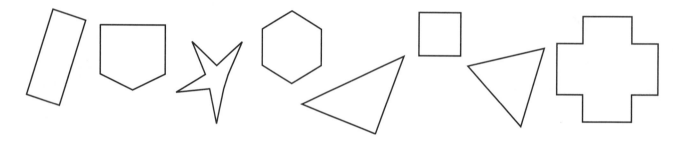

3 Name these angles.

a

_____

b

_____

c

_____

d

_____

e

_____

f

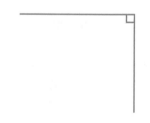

_____

For help with the questions on this page see
Understanding Maths: Geometry & Measurement **pages 4–6.**

4 Write whether each triangle is equilateral, isosceles or scalene.

a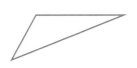

_____

b

_____

c

_____

d

_____

e

_____

f

_____

g

_____

h

_____

5 Which of the triangles in question 4 are right-angled triangles?   _____

6 Tick which of these pairs of lines are perpendicular.

a   b    c    d   e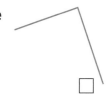

7 Name each of these quadrilaterals.

a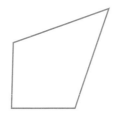

_____

b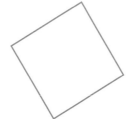

_____

c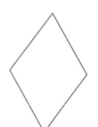

_____

d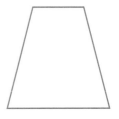

_____

8 Draw all the lines of reflective symmetry on each shape.

a 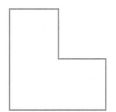   b 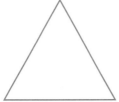   c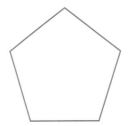

For help with the questions on this page see
Understanding Maths: Geometry & Measurement **pages 7–9.**

Geometry & Measurement

9 Write the co-ordinates of the positions of these letters on the grid.

   a P (___, ___)   **b** R (___, ___)

   c S (___, ___)   **d** T (___, ___)

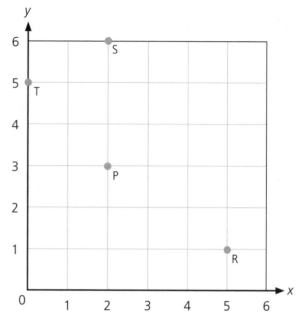

10 Mark these letters on the grid.

   a J at (**4**, **3**)   **b** K at (**5**, **5**)

   c L at (**1**, **1**)   **d** M at (**6**, **1**)

11 A shape has the co-ordinates (**1**, **2**) (**2**, **4**) and (**4**, **3**). Write its new co-ordinates after a translation of:

   a **2** squares to the right   (___, ___) (___, ___) (___, ___)

   b **4** squares up   (___, ___) (___, ___) (___, ___)

   c **1** square to the left and **2** squares down   (___, ___) (___, ___) (___, ___)

12 Use a protractor to measure the size of these angles.

   a _____

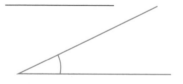

   b

   c

   d

13 Write the names of these shapes.

   a   **b** 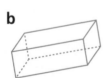   **c** 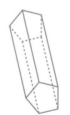   **d**   **e**

_____   _____   _____   _____   _____

For help with the questions on this page see
Understanding Maths: Geometry & Measurement **pages 11–14.**

Geometry & Measurement

14 Complete this table.

Name of shape	Number of faces (F)	Number of vertices (V)	Number of edges (E)
cube			
triangular prism			
square-based pyramid			
cylinder			
sphere			
cone			

15 Check Euler's Theorem for these shapes.

Shape	F	V	E + 2
cube			
cuboid			
triangular prism			
square-based pyramid			

16 Write the co-ordinates of these points.

a A (___,___)   **b** B (___,___)

c C (___,___)   **d** D (___,___)

17 Mark and label these points on the grid.

a E at (**–4**, **–3**)   **b** F at (**2**, **–3**)

c G at (**0**, **–2**)

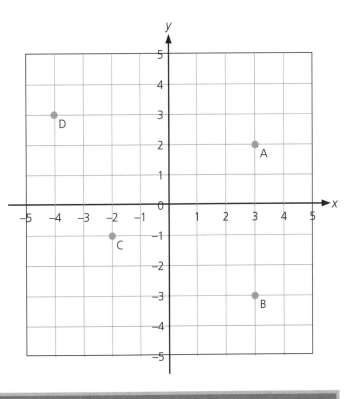

For help with the questions on this page see
Understanding Maths: Geometry & Measurement **pages 15–18.**

18 Colour the reflections of these patterns.

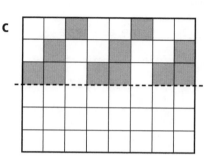

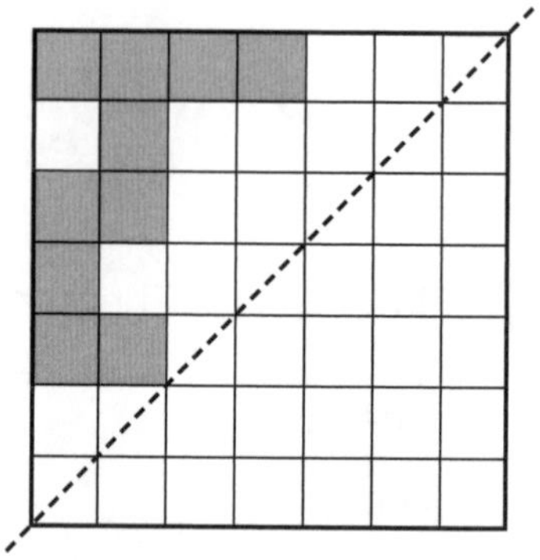

19 Shape D has the co-ordinates (**2**, **1**) (**2**, **4**) and (**1**, **2**). Write the co-ordinates of Shape D when it has been reflected in the:

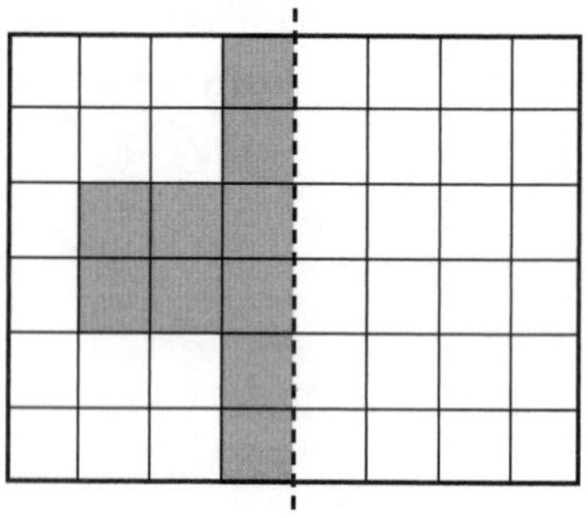

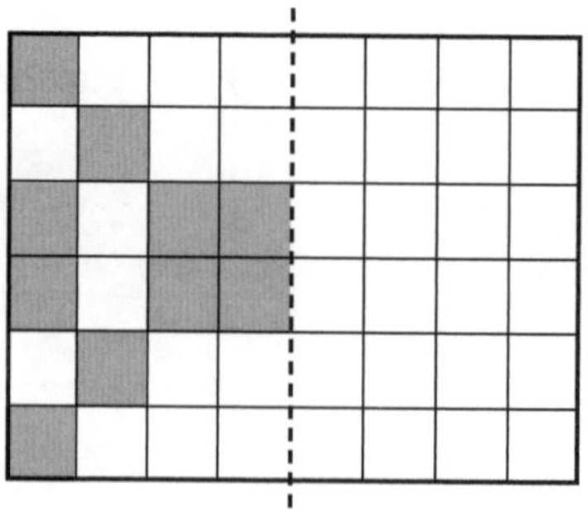

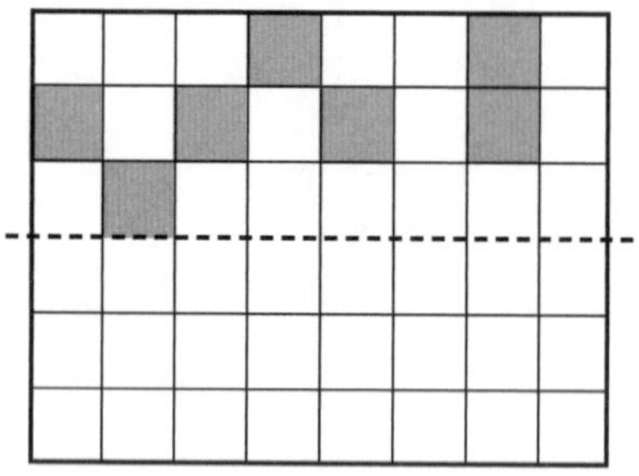

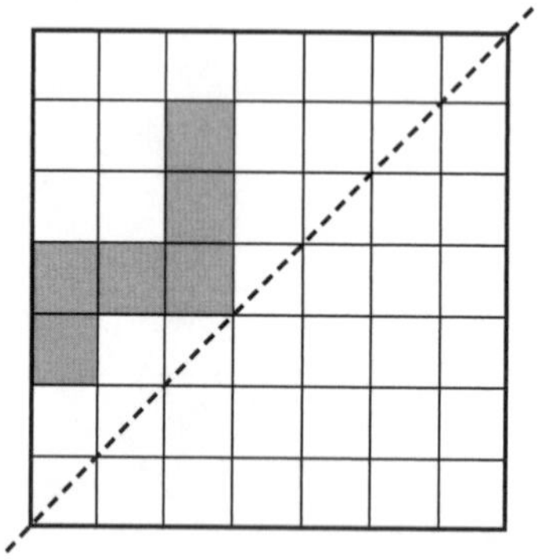

a *y* axis   (___ , ___)   (___ , ___)   (___ , ___)

b *x* axis   (___ , ___)   (___ , ___)   (___ , ___)

20 Calculate the missing angles.

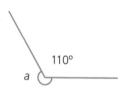 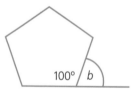 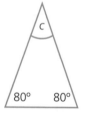 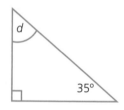

a = _____   *b* = _____   *c* = _____   *d* = _____

21 Write the correct word to name each red part of the circle.

a   **b**   **c**

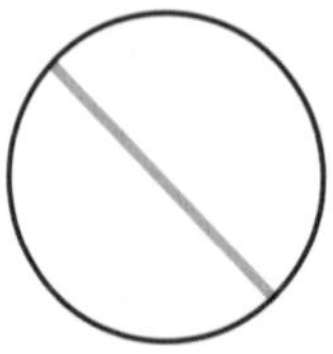

_____   _____   _____

For help with the questions on this page see
***Understanding Maths: Geometry & Measurement* pages 19–22.**

Geometry & Measurement

22 Fill in the missing numbers.

   a   **4**m = _____ cm   **b**   **2.5**cm = _____ mm

   c   **0.3**km = _____ m   **d**   **6.2**km = _____ m

23 Colour the best estimate for each item.

a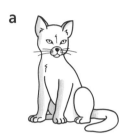

5g
5kg
50kg

b

20g
2kg
20kg

c

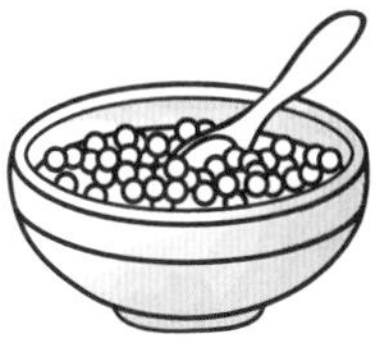

50g
1500g
10kg

24 Colour the best estimate for each item.

a

35ml
350ml
3.5l

b

1l
10l
100l

c

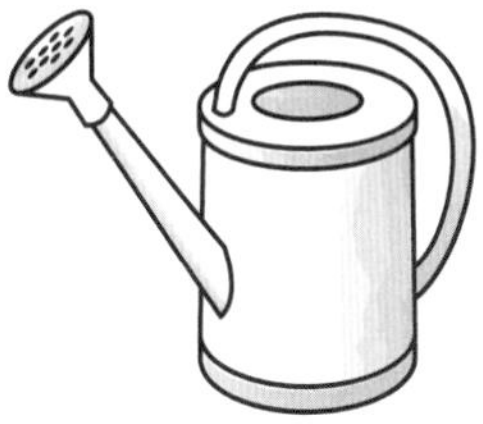

90ml
9l
90l

25 Convert these measurements.

   a   **5.2**kg = _____ g   **b**   **1.8**l = _____ ml

   c   **13 000**g = _____ kg   **d**   **8500**ml = _____ l

26 Write the numbers in the boxes to show what is being pointed to on these scales.

a

b

c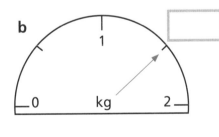

d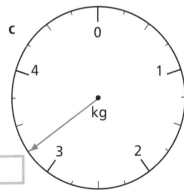

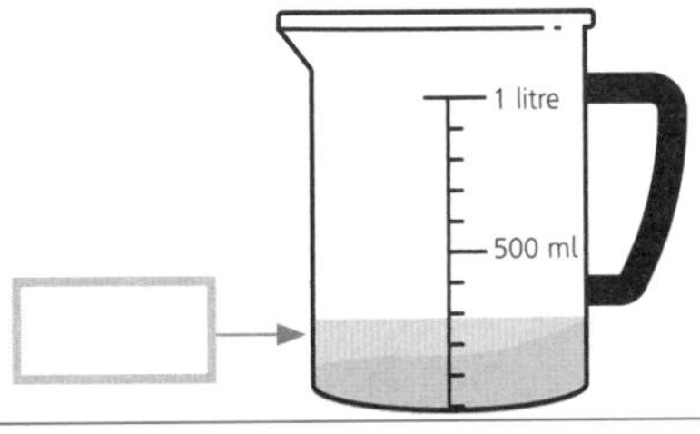

e

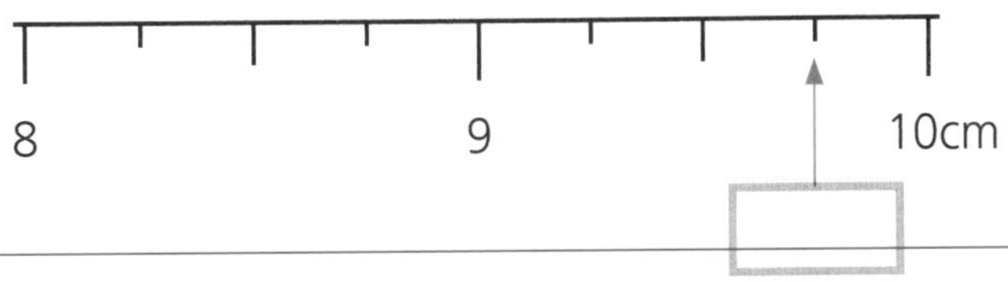

27 Find the perimeter of these shapes.

a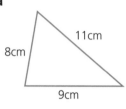

11cm
8cm
9cm

_____ cm

b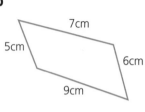

7cm
5cm
6cm
9cm

_____ cm

c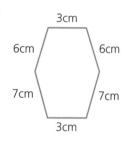

3cm
6cm   6cm
7cm   7cm
3cm

_____ cm

d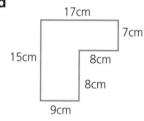

17cm
7cm
15cm   8cm
8cm
9cm

_____ cm

28 Join pairs of clocks showing the same times.

29

Cinema start times for Saturday			
	Odeon	**Centreplex**	**Moviedrome**
Club House	17:40	13:15	16:55
The Witch's Nose	16:30	17:05	17:20
Reality	18:30	19:45	19:30

Answer these questions using the information in the table above. Write the times in words, for example, twenty to eight in the evening.

a When does _The Witch's Nose_ start at the Centreplex?

_____

b When does _Club House_ start at the Odeon?

_____

c When does _Reality_ start at the Moviedrome?

_____

d If the time was 7 p.m. and you wanted to see _Reality_, which cinema would you go to?

_____

e If you arrived at the Odeon at 5 p.m., which film would be showing?

_____

For help with the questions on this page see
Understanding Maths: Geometry & Measurement **pages 30–34.**

Geometry & Measurement

30 Use the formula length × width = area to find the area of these rectangles.

a
12cm
8cm
_____ cm²

b
14cm
9cm
_____ cm²

c
15cm
11cm
_____ cm²

d
7cm
4cm
_____ cm²

e
8cm
5cm
_____ cm²

f
9cm
6cm
_____ cm²

31 Convert between these units.

a 1 foot = _____ inches

b 2 yards = _____ feet

c $\frac{1}{2}$ mile = _____ yards

d 1 gallon = _____ pints

e 10 pounds = _____ ounces

f 2 stone = _____ pounds

32 Convert between these units.

a 1 mile = _____ km

b 10 miles = _____ km

c _____ miles = **3.2**km

d _____ miles = **640**km

33 Find the area of these triangles (not to scale). Use the formula $\frac{1}{2}$ × base × height = area.

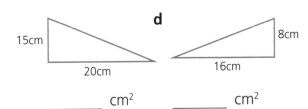

a
7cm
9cm
_____ cm²

b
12cm
8cm
_____ cm²

c
15cm
20cm
_____ cm²

d
8cm
16cm
_____ cm²

34 Find the area of these shapes by splitting them into rectangles (not drawn to scale).

a
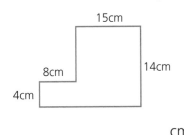
15cm
8cm
4cm
14cm
_____ cm²

b
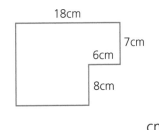
18cm
7cm
6cm
8cm
_____ cm²

c
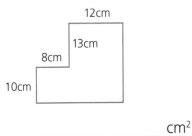
12cm
13cm
8cm
10cm
_____ cm²

For help with the questions on this page see
Understanding Maths: Geometry & Measurement pages 35–37.

Geometry & Measurement

35 Find the volume of these cuboids by counting cubes. Each cube drawn is **1cm³**.

a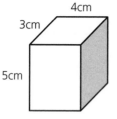

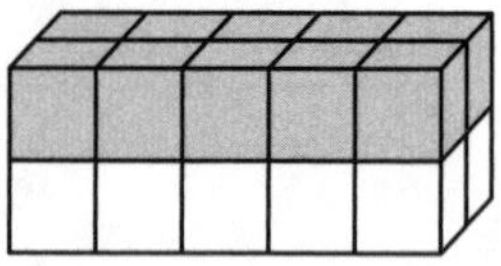

_____ cm³

b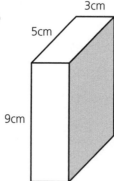

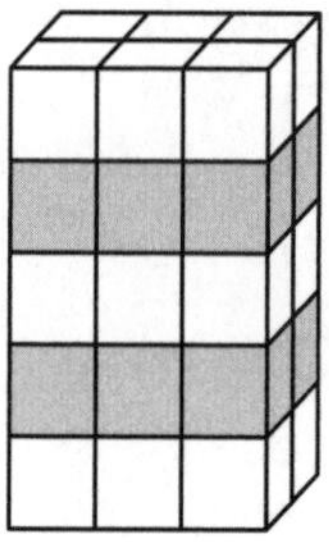

_____ cm³

36 Find the volume of these cuboids using length, width and height.

a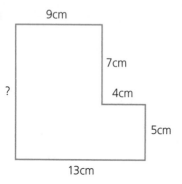

4cm
3cm
5cm

_____ cm³

b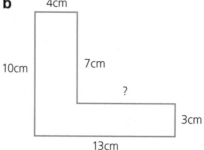

3cm
5cm
9cm

_____ cm³

37 Convert between these units.

a **3** minutes = _____ seconds

b **5** hours = _____ minutes

c **480** hours = _____ days

d **49** days = _____ weeks

e **36** months = _____ years

f **2** years = _____ days

38 Calculate the perimeter and area of each shape.

a
9cm
7cm
4cm
?
5cm
13cm

b
4cm
10cm
7cm
?
13cm
3cm

c
4cm
7cm
4cm
12cm
?
8cm

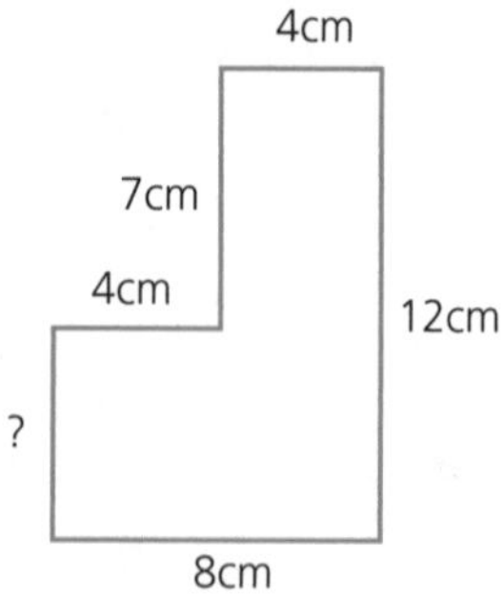

a perimeter = _____

area = _____

b perimeter = _____

area = _____

c perimeter = _____

area = _____

For help with the questions on this page see
Understanding Maths: Geometry & Measurement **pages 38–40.**

1 Draw a pictogram of this data, where ■ stands for **10** people.

Number of people in the café at these times	
Time	**Number of people**
10.00	30
12.00	35
2.00	10
4.00	25
6.00	5

10.00

12.00

2.00

4.00

6.00

2 Rachel counts the number of mobile phone calls she makes in one week. Draw a bar chart using the data in this frequency table.

Day	Number of calls
Mon	5
Tue	7
Wed	0
Thu	3
Fri	7
Sat	9
Sun	4

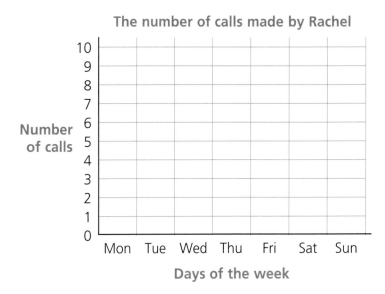

The number of calls made by Rachel

3 On which two days were the same number of calls made?

_____ and _____

4 Why might Rachel have made most calls on Saturday?

_____

5 What might have happened on Wednesday?

_____

For help with the questions on this page see
***Understanding Maths: Statistics* pages 5–10.**

Statistics

6 Write the value for each bar on these scales.

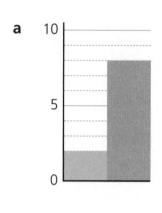

a
10
5
0

_____ _____

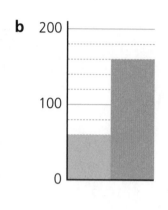

b
200
100
0

_____ _____

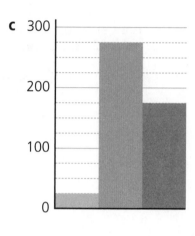

c
300
200
100
0

_____ _____ _____

7 Sort these numbers using this Venn diagram.

6	14
19	77
26	82
12	16
17	97
36	29

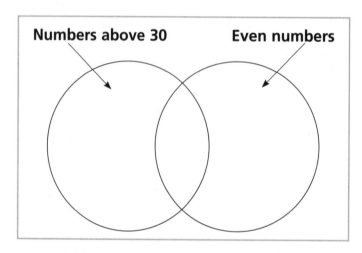

Numbers above 30   Even numbers

8 Sort these numbers using this Carroll diagram.

6	14
19	77
26	82
12	16
17	97
36	29

	Even	Not even
Numbers above 30	82	
Numbers that are not above 30		

For help with the questions on this page see
Understanding Maths: Statistics pages 12 and 14–15.

9 Look at this bar chart and answer the questions below.

A graph to show the number of cousins several children have

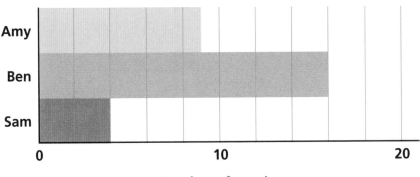

Number of cousins

a How many cousins has Sam? _____

b How many more cousins has Ben than Amy? _____

c How many cousins do the three children have in total? _____

10 The list below shows the ages of some people in a room.

a Complete the frequency table to show the information using grouped data.

87	15
22	32
31	46
35	23
18	7
74	45
47	53
29	90
66	32
44	9

Age	Tally	Frequency
0–29		
30–59		
60–89		
90+		

b Which age group has the most people? _____

c How many more **30–59** year olds are there than **60–89** year olds? _____

d How many fewer **0–29** year olds are there than **30–59** year olds? _____

For help with the questions on this page see
***Understanding Maths: Statistics* pages 13 and 16–17.**

Statistics

This bar line chart shows the positions during the race of the winner of the London Marathon. The race started at 10.00 a.m. Use this to answer questions 11–14.

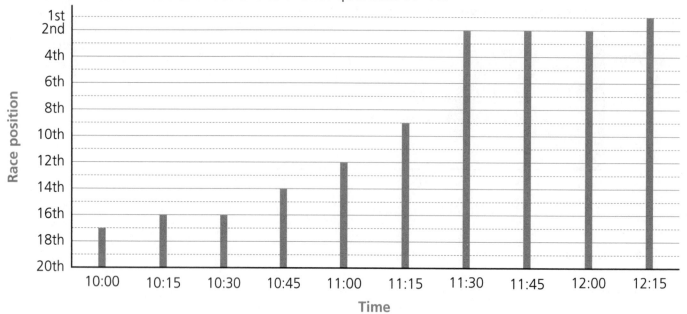

11 In which position was the winner at:

    a **10:00**? _____   b **11:15**? _____   c **12:00**? _____

12 At which time was the winner in:

    a **14**th position? _____   b **12**th position? _____

13 At what time was the winner in first position?   _____

14 By how many positions did the winner rise between **11:15** and **11:30**?   _____

15 Find the range of these sets of numbers.

    a 26, 54, 9, 17, 34, 6   _____   b 5, 17, 92, 37, 6, 2, 64, 18, 67, 25 _____

16 Find the mode of this set of numbers.

    5, 7, 2, 6, 3, 2, 5, 8, 9, 1, 5, 3   _____

17 Find the median of these sets of numbers.

    a 4, 8, 10, 3, 5, 4, 8   _____   b 3, 9, 4, 9, 2, 9, 6, 1, 2   _____

18 Find the mean of these sets of numbers.

    a 4, 6, 8, 3, 2, 10, 7, 8   _____   b 11, 5, 3, 8, 2, 2, 9, 4, 5, 11   _____

> **For help with the questions on this page see**
> *Understanding Maths: Statistics* pages 19–23.

Statistics

19 The mean of these cards is **5**.
What is the missing number?

| 2 | 7 | 3 | 8 | 4 | |

20 Find the mean, median and mode of these sets of numbers.

a 12 12 7 4 5 12 12 4 4   mean _____ median _____ mode _____

b 13 10 12 15 14 17 14 17   mean _____ median _____ mode _____

21 Estimate the value for each cross marked on these scales.

a

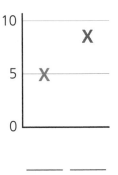

_____ _____

b

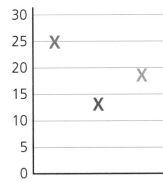

_____ _____ _____

c

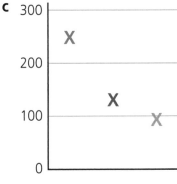

_____ _____ _____

22 Draw a line graph using the data in this table. It shows the temperature in a greenhouse during a 12-hour period.

Time of day	Temperature °C
06:00	7
08:00	12
10:00	19
12:00	28
14:00	35
16:00	31
18:00	24

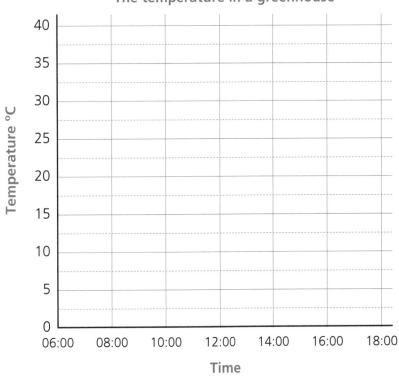

The temperature in a greenhouse

For help with the questions on this page see
Understanding Maths: Statistics pages 23–26.

Statistics

Alfie and Jake were throwing stones into the sea. The graph shows the heights above sea-level of the stones from the moment they were thrown. Use this to answer questions 23–26.

Time (seconds)		0	0.5	1	1.5	2	2.5	3	3.5	4	4.5	5	5.5	6	6.5	7	7.5	8
Height (m)	Alfie's	2	6	12	16	20	23	26	25	22	19	14	9	4	0	0	0	0
	Jake's	2	5	9	13	16	19	21	19.5	17	14	11	2	0	0	0	0	0

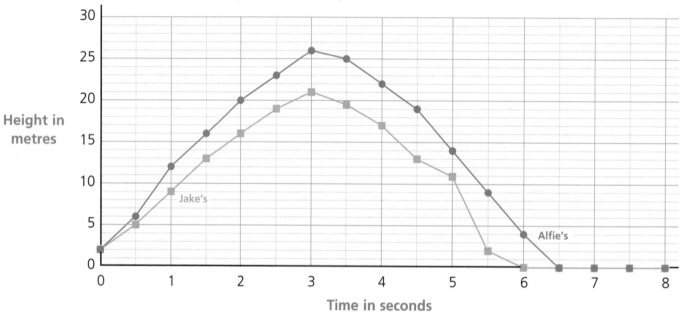

A line graph to show heights above sea-level of the two stones

23 At what height was Jake's stone after:

a **1** second? _____ b **3** seconds? _____ c **5** seconds? _____

24 At what height was Alfie's stone after:

a **1** second? _____ b **3.5** seconds? _____ c **5** seconds? _____

25 At about what times do you think the height of Jake's stone was:

a **13**m? _____ b **2**m? _____

26 At about what times do you think the height of Alfie's stone was:

a **12**m? _____ b **23**m? _____

For help with the questions on this page see
Understanding Maths: Statistics page 27.

Statistics

This is part of a bus timetable from Newcastle to Sunderland. Use this to answer questions 27–29.

Monday to Friday						
Newcastle Monument	11:20	11:35	11:50	12:05	12:20	12:35
Gateshead Metro	11:30	11:45	12:00	12:15	12:30	12:45
Queen Elizabeth Hospital	11:40	11:55	12:10	12:25	12:40	12:55
Donwell	11:55	12:10	12:25	12:40	12:55	13:10
Nissan Factory	12:09	12:24	12:39	12:54	13:09	13:24
Southwick	12:19	12:34	12:49	13:04	13:19	13:34
Sunderland Interchange	12:32	12:47	13:02	13:17	13:32	13:47

27 How long does it take to get from:

   a Newcastle Monument to Queen Elizabeth Hospital?   _____

   b Donwell to Southwick?   _____

   c Southwick to Sunderland Interchange?   _____

28 Keira left Donwell at **12:55**. What time did she get to Southwick?   _____

29 Ali walked to Gateshead Metro, arriving at **12:35**. What time was the next bus?   _____

Distance in kilometres

Aberdeen				
630	**Bristol**			
702	275	**Dover**		
405	230	355	**Manchester**	
641	160	117	263	**London**

30 Use the table to find the distance in kilometres from:

   a Aberdeen to Dover   _____   **b** London to Bristol _____

   c Manchester to Aberdeen _____   **d** Dover to Bristol _____

For help with the questions on this page see
Understanding Maths: Statistics **pages 29–30.**

Statistics

31 Use the conversion graph to approximately convert:

a 4 miles to kilometres _____   **b 2.5** miles to kilometres _____

c 5 kilometres to miles _____   **d 4** kilometres to miles _____

This conversion graph converts
between miles and kilometres.

| **1** mile = 1.6km (approx.) |

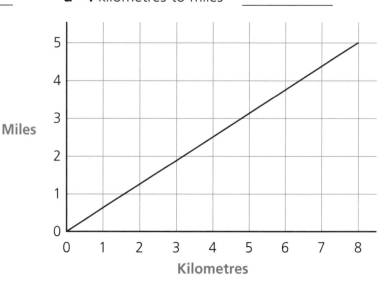

32 How many of the people surveyed were:

a left-handed females? _____   **b** right-handed males? _____

c left-handed? _____   **d** males? _____

A survey asked some people whether they were right-handed
or left-handed. The results are shown here.

	Handed	
	Left	Right
Female	9	52
Male	11	47

33 How many people were surveyed in total in question 32? _____

34 Look at this pie chart. It shows how the money earned by
a leisure centre came from different activities. About what
fraction came from each activity?

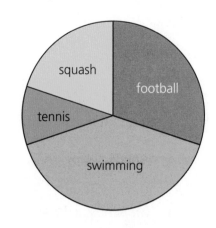

a squash _____

b swimming _____

c tennis _____

d football _____

For help with the questions on this page see
Understanding Maths: Statistics pages 31–34.

Practice

35 This pie chart shows how Farmer Philpot uses his land.
About what fraction of his land is used to grow:

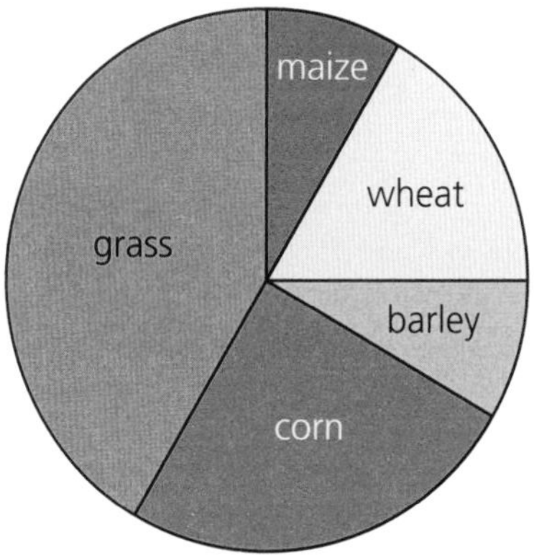

a grass?   _____

b corn?   _____

c wheat?   _____

d barley?   _____

36 This pie chart shows how Farmer Brown uses his **180** acres of land.
Measure the angle for:

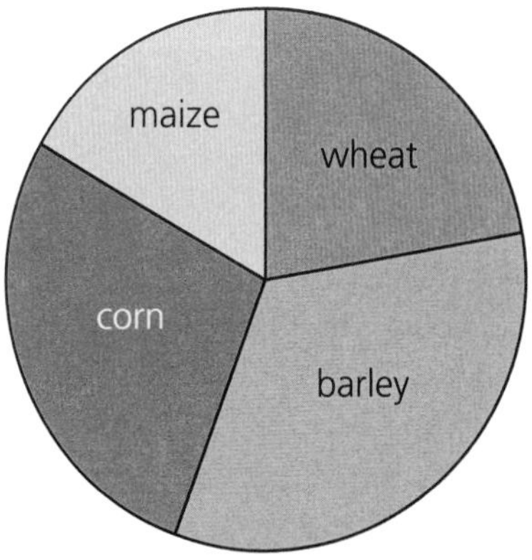

a wheat?   _____

b barley?   _____

c corn?   _____

d maize?   _____

37 Write what fraction of the whole pie in question 36 is:

a wheat   b barley   c corn   d maize

38 Now find how many acres of Farmer Browns's land is:

a wheat _____   b barley _____

c corn _____   d maize _____

For help with the questions on this page see
***Understanding Maths: Statistics* pages 34–36.**

39 Draw a pie chart of the information in this table.
You will need a protractor.

This table shows the favourite
colour of **100** children.

Colour	Number of children
red	45
blue	25
yellow	15
green	10
other	5

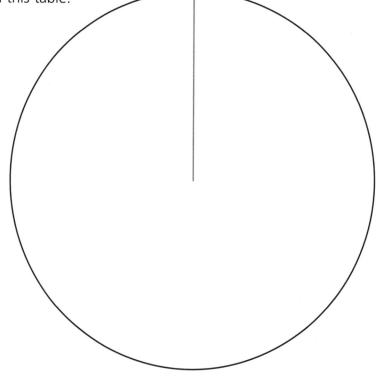

40 Draw a scatter graph to show the number of cold drinks sold per hour by a seaside shop according to the outside temperature.

Temperature °C	0	4	8	12	16	20	24	28	32	36
Number of cold drinks sold each hour	1	4	7	12	19	28	36	42	48	59

Sales of cold drinks

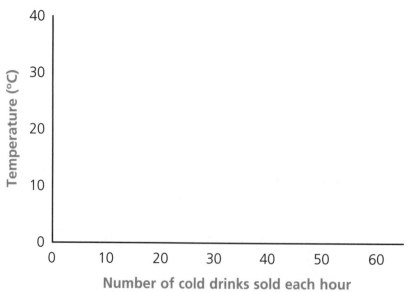

For help with the questions on this page see
Understanding Maths: Statistics pages 37–40.

Answers

Addition & Subtraction

Page 4

1
a 40   b 40   c 60
d 100   e 100   f 100

2
a 85   b 65
c 25   d 10

3
a 1000   b 1000
c 300   d 900

4
a row: 16, 18, 14   column: 17, 16, 15
b row: 18, 20, 18   column: 15, 24, 17

5
a row: 23, 28, 31, 37   column: 21, 42, 23, 33
b row: 22, 33, 31, 34   column: 35, 28, 32, 25

Page 5

6
a 12
b 19
c 28
d 36

7 The start and finish numbers are the same because for each addition there is a similar subtraction that undoes it and for each subtraction there is a similar addition that undoes it. This works because addition and subtraction are inverses.

8
a 17   b 39   c 19

9
a 47   b 63   c 43
d 45   e 77   f 97
g 430   h 730   i 650

Page 6

10
a 33, 43, 53
b 35, 45, 55
c 9, 19, 29
d 12, 120, 1200
e 15, 150, 1500
f 1, 91, 991

11
a 96   b 94
c 93   d 91

12
a 65   b 65   c 77
d 94   e 87   f 131

Page 7

13
a 9   b 19   c 19
d 25   e 17   f 20

14
a 9   b 9   c 8
d 12   e 11   f 11

15
a 66   b 49   c 81
d 161   e 245   f 379
g 551   h 526   i 682
j 314   k 403   l 580
m 379   n 376   o 584
p 675   q 888   r 981

16
a 44   b 56   c 75
d 302   e 483   f 569
g 59   h 118   i 281
j 359   k 399   l 558

17
a 341   b 530   c 641
d 709   e 1121   f 1088

Page 8

18
a 242   b 422   c 513
d 313   e 231   f 221
g 208   h 492   i 392
j 330   k 377   l 277

19
a 598   b 634
c 582   d 146
e 77   f 153
g 54769   h 28623
i 52467   j 91055
k 27122   l 35162
m 14739   n 34498

20
a 3110   b 4824
c 34661   d 23023
e 47061   f 10623

Page 9

21 a 4000 + 2000 = 6000
b 7000 − 4000 = 3000
c 9000 − 4000 = 5000
d 3000 + 5000 = 8000

22 a 5931
b 3076
c 4744
d 8038

23 a 5931 − 3878; or 5931 − 2053
b 3076 + 3855
c 4121 + 4744
d 8038 − 4853; or 8038 − 3185

24 a 5191   b 5961
c 5627   d 8407

25 a 862   b 6032
c 4092   d 6513

Page 10

26 a 20 or twenty   b 2 or two
c 200000 or 2 hundred thousand
d 20000 or 20 thousand
e 2000000 or 2 million
f 2000 or 2 thousand

27 a 4707106
b 9111810
c 2012045

28 a 838512
b 4042008

29 a 454245   b 453857
c 459157   d 653257
e 1575148   f 1445008

30 a 555247   b 166811
c 1455234   d 561890

Page 11

31 a 78.81   b 89.04   c 93.81

32 a £70.88   b £83.44   c £93.85

33 a 11.5   b 14.52   c 43.78

34 a £15.34   b £29.79   c £56.21

35 9877

36 £2.57

37 2722

Page 12

38 a 1830mm
b £1738
c 8768

39 a £40.56
b £14873008

40 a 96.7cm
b 1328.9g or 1.3289kg
c 40.9kg

Multiplication & Division

Page 13

1 a 50   b 50   c 28   d 28
e 27   f 27   g 30   h 30
i 6   j 2   k 3   l 4
m 5   n 4   o 3   p 8

2 a 4   b 10   c 20
d 30   e 4   f 21

3
27	32	0	28
90	80	6	24
25	12	20	40
21	15	8	36
30	45	40	18
12	16	18	24
35	16	10	15

Page 14

4 3, 6, 9, 12, 15, 18, 21, 24, 27, 30, 33, 36

5 a 9   b 12   c 6   d 6
e 8   f 9   g 7   h 9
i 11   j 11   k 11   l 6

6   **a** 8
     b 9
     c 7
     d 45
     e 48

7   **a** 14
     b 9
     c 70km

8   **a** 34   **b** 48   **c** 64   **d** 92   **e** 96
     f 108   **g** 134   **h** 146   **i** 172   **j** 190

Page 15

9   72   81   45   48
     30   90   42   56
     49   36   28   56
     72   70   54   35
     64   63   24   63
     18   40   54   48

10   3   4   5   7
     5   4   5   6
     6   6   8   7
     8   7   9   10
     8   7   6   8
     9   9   7   9

11   **a** 44   **b** 84   **c** 66   **d** 96
     e 8   **f** 3   **g** 3   **h** 5
     i 12   **j** 121   **k** 144   **l** 1
     m 99   **n** 108   **o** 8   **p** 10
     q 110   **r** 72   **s** 9   **t** 11

Page 16

12   **a** 6   **b** 5
     c 9   **d** 32

13   **a** 1   **b** 12
     c 1   **d** 16

14   **a** 70   **b** 80   **c** 90
     d 130   **e** 140   **f** 200

15   **a** 80   **b** 230   **c** 390
     d 750   **e** 2160   **f** 4620
     g 5890   **h** 42 080   **i** 62 900

16   **a** 500p   **b** 1800p   **c** 7600p
     d 25 400p   **e** 196 800p   **f** 209 700p

Page 17

17   **a** 120   **b** 120   **c** 56
     d 320   **e** 45   **f** 0

18   **a** 8   **b** 12   **c** 39
     d 47   **e** 78   **f** 95
     g 387   **h** 428   **i** 985

19   **a** £2   **b** £6   **c** £8
     d £15   **e** £23   **f** £45
     g £56   **h** £257   **i** £500

20   **a** 4m   **b** 7.5m   **c** 12.5m
     d 34m   **e** 68m   **f** 87m
     g 91m   **h** 548m   **i** 3208m

21   **a** 14   **b** 32   **c** 50   **d** 100
     e 24   **f** 8   **g** 32   **h** 16

Page 18

22   **a** 415   **b** 342   **c** 276

23   **a** 800   **b** 1200
     c 4000   **d** 4200

24   **a** 1299   **b** 1284
     c 2070   **d** 3542

25   **a** 5 r1   **b** 3 r1   **c** 6 r1
     d 8 r1   **e** 9 r2   **f** 10 r1
     g 4 r2   **h** 6 r1   **i** 7 r2
     j 8 r3   **k** 9 r1   **l** 10 r3

26   **a** 11   **b** 9
     c 7   **d** 5

Page 19

27   **a** 16   **b** 25   **c** 100
     d 8   **e** 125   **f** 1000

28   **a** 40, 72, 112
     b 56, 35, 91

29   **a** 104cm²   **b** 144cm²

30   **a** 1389   **b** 2635   **c** 1944
     d 1316   **e** 3512   **f** 2547

Page 20

31   **a** 2315   **b** 2288   **c** 2916
     d 1428   **e** 3090   **f** 4356

32   **a** 11 780   **b** 43 533   **c** 59 776
     d 12 744   **e** 38 003   **f** 50 992

33   **a** 27   **b** 23   **c** 21
     d 63   **e** 47   **f** 57

34   **a** 2114   **b** 2161
     c 1615   **d** 1499

Page 21

35   **a** 200 × 4 = 800   **36**   **a** 772
     b 200 ÷ 5 = 40   **b** 43

37   **a** 772 ÷ 4 = 193
     b 5 × 43 = 215

38   **a** 934 r4   **b** 734 r1
     c 1434 r1   **d** 407 r6

39   **a** $1256\frac{1}{4}$
     b $1367\frac{4}{7}$

40   **a** 9
     b 8

Page 22

41   **a** 1116   **b** 1729
     c 3415   **d** 7792
     e 39 072   **f** 43 884

42   **a** 11 989   **b** 9468   **c** 22 554
     d 23 166   **e** 27 744   **f** 38 584
     g 143 475   **h** 316 692   **i** 787 611

43   **a** 488.5   **b** 658.25
     c 1095.75   **d** 846.6

44   **a** 419 r4   **b** 448 r9

Page 23

45   **a** 36   **b** 78
     c 5670   **d** 4230
     e 0.327   **f** 0.46
     g 0.53   **h** 0.7

46   **a** 10.4   **b** 44.88
     c 98.07   **d** 68.88

47   **a** 21.8   **b** 1.34

48   £12

49   **a** 11, 8   **b** 21, 19

Fractions

Page 24

1   **a** $\frac{1}{5}$ **b** $\frac{1}{7}$ **c** $\frac{1}{10}$ **d** $\frac{1}{12}$

2   **a** 1 part shaded
     b 1 part shaded
     c 2 parts shaded

3   Only **a** and **f** fractions are correctly named.

4   **a** 8   **b** 4   **c** 4   **d** 2

5   **a** £16   **b** 8
     c 5   **d** 20

Answers continued

Page 25

6   **a** $\frac{8}{12}$ or $\frac{4}{6}$ or $\frac{2}{3}$ **b** $\frac{6}{15}$ or $\frac{2}{5}$

7   **a** $6\frac{1}{2}$, 7, $7\frac{1}{2}$, 8, $8\frac{1}{2}$, 9

    b $3\frac{1}{2}$, $3\frac{3}{4}$, 4, $4\frac{1}{4}$, $4\frac{1}{2}$, $4\frac{3}{4}$

    c $9\frac{1}{4}$, 9, $8\frac{3}{4}$, $8\frac{1}{2}$, $8\frac{1}{4}$, 8

8   **a** 8   **b** 12   **c** 12   **d** 15

9   **a** 6   **b** 9   **c** 20   **d** 25

    e 30   **f** 30   **g** 21   **h** 56

10   **a** $\frac{5}{10}$, $\frac{6}{10}$, $\frac{8}{10}$, $\frac{13}{10}$, $\frac{14}{10}$

    b $1\frac{3}{10}$, $1\frac{4}{10}$, $1\frac{6}{10}$, $1\frac{7}{10}$, $1\frac{8}{10}$, $1\frac{9}{10}$

11   **a** $\frac{7}{10}$ **b** $\frac{9}{10}$ **c** $1\frac{1}{10}$ or $\frac{11}{10}$

Page 26

12   **a** $\frac{11}{10}$ **b** $\frac{11}{9}$

    c $\frac{7}{6}$ **d** $\frac{13}{8}$

13   **a** $1\frac{2}{4}$ or $1\frac{1}{2}$ **b** $1\frac{3}{7}$

    c $2\frac{3}{10}$ **d** $1\frac{5}{6}$

14   **a** $1\frac{3}{4}$ **b** $2\frac{4}{5}$

    c $1\frac{3}{10}$ **d** $2\frac{3}{7}$

15   **a** >   **b** <   **c** >

    d <   **e** >   **f** >

16   **a** $\frac{6}{7}$, $\frac{3}{4}$, $\frac{3}{5}$, $\frac{1}{2}$, $\frac{1}{3}$

    b $\frac{9}{10}$, $\frac{4}{5}$, $\frac{7}{10}$, $\frac{3}{5}$, $\frac{1}{4}$, $\frac{1}{5}$

Page 27

17   **a** fractions equivalent to $\frac{1}{2}$, such as $\frac{2}{4}$, $\frac{5}{10}$

    b fractions equivalent to $\frac{1}{5}$, such as $\frac{2}{10}$, $\frac{3}{15}$, $\frac{4}{20}$, $\frac{10}{50}$

    c fractions equivalent to $\frac{2}{3}$, such as $\frac{4}{6}$, $\frac{6}{9}$, $\frac{8}{12}$, $\frac{20}{30}$

18   **a** >   **b** >   **c** =

    d >   **e** <   **f** =

19   **a** $\frac{5}{100}$, $\frac{6}{100}$, $\frac{7}{100}$, $\frac{8}{100}$, $\frac{9}{100}$, $\frac{12}{100}$, $\frac{13}{100}$

    b $2\frac{2}{100}$, $2\frac{3}{100}$, $2\frac{5}{100}$, $2\frac{6}{100}$, $2\frac{7}{100}$, $2\frac{8}{100}$, $2\frac{9}{100}$

20   **a** $\frac{9}{100}$ **b** $\frac{45}{100}$ **c** $\frac{80}{100}$

21   **a** $\frac{1}{4}$, 5   **b** $\frac{1}{2}$, 11

    c $\frac{3}{5}$, 15   **d** $\frac{7}{10}$, 84

Page 28

22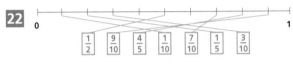

23   **a** $\frac{1}{9}$, $\frac{3}{9}$ (or $\frac{1}{3}$), $\frac{5}{9}$, $\frac{6}{9}$ (or $\frac{2}{3}$), $\frac{7}{9}$

    b $\frac{1}{12}$, $\frac{2}{12}$ (or $\frac{1}{6}$), $\frac{2}{6}$ (or $\frac{1}{3}$), $\frac{5}{12}$, $\frac{7}{12}$, $\frac{2}{3}$, $\frac{5}{6}$

24   **a** 6, $\frac{3}{4}$

    b 8, $\frac{2}{11}$

    c 14, $\frac{3}{4}$

25   **a** $4\frac{1}{2}$ **b** $2\frac{1}{3}$ **c** $1\frac{3}{5}$ **d** $2\frac{3}{4}$

    e $2\frac{1}{10}$ **f** $1\frac{5}{8}$ **g** $3\frac{1}{6}$ **h** $6\frac{3}{4}$

    i $3\frac{1}{7}$ **j** $3\frac{4}{8}$ or $3\frac{1}{2}$ **k** $4\frac{7}{9}$ **l** $5\frac{7}{10}$

Page 29

26   **a** $\frac{49}{9}$ **b** $\frac{27}{4}$ **c** $\frac{52}{7}$ **d** $\frac{44}{5}$

    e $\frac{83}{9}$ **f** $\frac{117}{10}$ **g** $\frac{103}{8}$ **h** $\frac{107}{7}$

27 $\frac{35}{9} = 3\frac{8}{9}$, $6\frac{5}{9} = \frac{59}{9}$, $\frac{51}{9} = 5\frac{6}{9}$

28   **a** $\frac{1}{3}$ **b** $\frac{1}{2}$ **c** $\frac{1}{3}$ **d** $\frac{1}{7}$

29   **a** $\frac{8}{9}$ **b** $\frac{7}{8}$

30   **a** $2\frac{1}{2}$ **b** $3\frac{2}{3}$

31 a $\frac{8}{10}$, $\frac{7}{10}$, larger $\frac{4}{5}$

b $\frac{6}{8}$, $\frac{7}{8}$, larger $\frac{7}{8}$

c $\frac{6}{16}$, $\frac{7}{16}$, larger $\frac{7}{16}$

d $\frac{4}{10}$, $\frac{3}{10}$, larger $\frac{2}{5}$

e $\frac{15}{20}$, $\frac{16}{20}$, larger $\frac{4}{5}$

f $\frac{15}{18}$, $\frac{14}{18}$, larger $\frac{5}{6}$

g $\frac{3}{9}$, $\frac{2}{9}$, larger $\frac{1}{3}$

h $\frac{15}{21}$, $\frac{14}{21}$, larger $\frac{5}{7}$

i $\frac{18}{21}$, $\frac{19}{21}$, larger $\frac{19}{21}$

32 a $\frac{7}{9}$ b $\frac{13}{16}$ c $\frac{5}{6}$

Page 30

33 a $\frac{3}{9}$ $\left(\frac{1}{3}\right)$, $\frac{5}{9}$, $\frac{6}{9}$ $\left(\frac{2}{3}\right)$

b $\frac{2}{8}$ $\left(\frac{1}{4}\right)$, $\frac{3}{8}$, $\frac{5}{8}$

c $\frac{2}{12}$ $\left(\frac{1}{6}\right)$, $\frac{3}{12}$ $\left(\frac{1}{4}\right)$, $\frac{4}{12}$ $\left(\frac{1}{3}\right)$

d $\frac{16}{20}$ $\left(\frac{4}{5}\right)$, $\frac{18}{20}$ $\left(\frac{9}{10}\right)$, $\frac{19}{20}$

34 a $2\frac{8}{9}$ b $7\frac{7}{8}$

c $4\frac{1}{15}$ d $3\frac{1}{12}$

35 a $4\frac{7}{9}$ b $7\frac{6}{10}$ or $7\frac{3}{5}$

c $3\frac{5}{7}$ d $1\frac{4}{5}$

36 a $\frac{2}{15}$ b $\frac{2}{7}$

37 a $\frac{3}{10}$ b $\frac{1}{4}$

c $\frac{3}{5}$ d $\frac{15}{28}$

Decimals & Percentages

Page 31

1 a 3.5   b 4.7   c 2.9

d 16.4   e 53.2   f 36.8

g 9.32   h 7.19   i 26.76

2 a 6.37   b 5.82   c 9.79

d 17.32   e 45.21   f 128.08

g 5.569   h 8.307   i 15.792

3 a 7 hundredths   b 5 tenths   c 1 tenth

d 6 hundredths   e 9 tenths   f 3 hundredths

4 a 0.9   b 0.4

c 0.43   d 0.25

5 a 1.3   b 73.2

c 4.3   d 0.08

e 50.3   f 2.61

Page 32

6 a
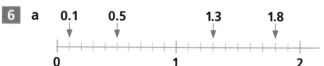

b
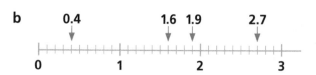

c
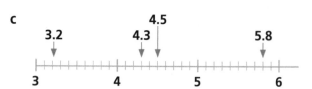

7 a 3   b 4   c 6

d 8   e 12   f 9

8 a <   b >

c >   d <

e >   f >

g <   h <

9 a 3.2kg in lower pan

b 4.65kg in lower pan

c 6.87kg in lower pan

10 a 0.2, 0.5, 0.8, 0.9

b 0.03, 0.06, 0.07, 0.08

Answers continued

Page 33

11 **a** 0.01, 0.08 **b** 0.13, 0.17

12 **a** 12 **b** 19 **c** 20

13 **a** 0.53 **b** 0.7 **c** 0.9
     d 0.21 **e** 0.61 **f** 0.8

14 **a** 0.36, 0.6, 0.65, 0.7
     b 0.8, 0.85, 0.9, 0.93
     c 0.48, 0.49, 0.5, 0.51
     d 1.5, 1.56, 1.57, 1.6
     e 2.35, 2.45, 2.53, 2.54

15 **a** 0.52kg, 0.5kg, 0.40kg, 0.34kg
     b 8.0m, 7.9m, 7.6m, 6.5m

Page 34

16 **a** $\frac{3}{4}$ **b** $\frac{3}{5}$ **c** $\frac{7}{10}$ **d** $\frac{1}{2}$

17 **a** 40.8
     b 63.1
     c 70.0
     d 89.65
     e 117.96

18 **a** 42.6
     b 13.6
     c 45.5
     d 19.65
     e 7.73

19 **a** 4.8m
     b 6.3cm

20 0.002

21 **a** 0.174, 0.3, 0.35, 0.53, 0.573
     b 8.238, 8.368, 8.391, 8.73, 8.8

22 **a** 550p, £5.20, £5.05, £5.02, £5
     b 7.653g, 6.75g, 6.57g, 5.762g, 5.72g

Page 35

23 **a** 1.983km
     b 1.393kg

24 **a** 20% **b** 20% **c** 25%

25 **a** 8 **b** 14 **c** 20
     d 48 **e** 125 **f** 200

26 **a** 3 **b** 5 **c** 10
     d 20 **e** 35 **f** 125

27 **a** 6 **b** 12 **c** 27
     d 57 **e** 150 **f** 4500

28 **a** £13 **b** 35g **c** 258m

29 **a** £9 **b** 45kg **c** 240m

30 **a** £36 **b** 90km **c** 225cm

Page 36

31

Percentage	Decimal	Fraction
30%	0.3	$\frac{3}{10}$
70%	0.7	$\frac{7}{10}$
20%	**0.2**	$\frac{2}{10}$ or $\frac{1}{5}$
80%	0.8	$\frac{8}{10}$ or $\frac{4}{5}$
60%	**0.6**	$\frac{6}{10}$ or $\frac{3}{5}$
40%	0.4	$\frac{4}{10}$ or $\frac{2}{5}$
100%	1.0	1
10%	**0.1**	$\frac{1}{10}$

32 **a** 0.42 **b** 0.35 **c** 0.63
     d 0.03 **e** 0.99 **f** 1.0

33 **a** 46% **b** 87% **c** 91%
     d 70% **e** 80% **f** 1%

34 **a** 15
     b 36

35 **a** £58.50 **b** £30.72
     c £21.32 **d** 124.8kg
     e 175.54kg **f** 100.92kg

Page 37

36 a 0.8   b 0.04
    c 3   d 1.7
    e 8   f 36

37 a 0.125 = 12.5%
    b 0.375 = 37.5%

38 a 3.2   b 0.35
    c 4.5   d 0.18
    e 0.63   f 0.064
    g 0.4   h 0.02

39 a 0.08   b 1.2
    c 0.9   d 0.04

40 a 0.67   b 0.89
    c 0.27   d 0.37
    e 0.11   f 0.53

Number Patterns & Algebra

Page 38

1 a 102, 112, 122, 132, 142, 152, 162, 172, 182, 192

    b 213, 203, 193, 183, 173, 163, 153, 143, 133, 123

    c 472, 462, 452, 442, 432, 422, 412, 402, 392, 382

2 a 704, 804, 904, 1004, 1104, 1204, 1304, 1404, 1504, 1604

    b 1942, 2042, 2142, 2242, 2342, 2442, 2542, 2642, 2742, 2842

3 a 4279, 4179, 4079, 3979, 3879, 3779, 3679, 3579, 3479, 3379

    b 9302, 9202, 9102, 9002, 8902, 8802, 8702, 8602, 8502, 8402

4 a 6553, 6453, 6353, 6253, 6153, 6053, 5953, 5853, 5753, 5653

    b 10073, 9973, 9873, 9773, 9673, 9573, 9473, 9373, 9273, 9173

    c 7421, 7521, 7621, 7721, 7821, 7921, 8021, 8121, 8221, 8321

5 12, 15, 18, 21, 24, 27, 30, 33, 36, 39, 42

6 48, 44, 40, 36, 32, 28, 24, 20, 16, 12, 8

7 55, 50, 45, 40, 35, 30, 25, 20, 15, 10, 5

Page 39

8 a 32, 40, 44, 96

    b 24, 36, 48, 30, 78, 96

9   52   62

 34   81

10 a 950, 975, 1000, 1025, 1050, 1075, 1100

    b 3900, 4000, 4100, 4200, 4300, 4400, 4500

    c 50: 1500, 1550, 1600, 1650, 1700, 1750, 1800

11 a 63, 49, 35, 28

    b 42, 54, 66

    c 99, 81, 63, 36

Page 40

12 a 81, 63, 36, 45, 72, 54, 99

    b 49, 56, 70, 28, 112

13 a 27, 34, 41, 48, 55, 62

    b 15, 23, 31, 39, 47, 55

    c 136, 127, 118, 109, 100, 91

    d 237, 224, 211, 198, 185, 172

14 a 91, 84, 77, 70, 63, 56, 49, 42

    b −6, 22, 50, 78, 106, 134, 162, 190

15 a 25, 36, square numbers

    b 60, 73, 86, counting up in 13s

    c −3, −9, −15, counting down in 6s

16 a 8, $7\frac{2}{3}$, $7\frac{1}{3}$, starting with 9 and counting back in thirds

    b $4\frac{1}{2}$, $4\frac{3}{4}$, 5, starting at $3\frac{3}{4}$ and adding quarters

Answers continued

Page 41

17 **a** 0.04, 0.09, 0.12

    b 0.9, 0.92, 1

18 **a** 2.1, 2.4, 2.7, 3.0, 3.3, 3.6, 3.9

    b 1.5, 1.75, 2.0, 2.25, 2.5, 2.75, 3.0

19 **a** –6, –4, –2, 0, 2, 4, 6, 8

    b –7, –5, –3, –1, 1, 3, 5, 7

20 **a** 3, 1, –1, –3, –5, –7, –9, –11

    b –2, –5, –8, –11, –14, –17, –20, –23

21 **a** 5°C   **b** 6°C

    c 16°C   **d** 16°C

22 **a** –5°C, –3°C, –1°C, 1°C, 5°C

    b –10°C, –4°C, –1°C, 0°C, 9°C

23 **a** 6cm

    b 8cm

    c 12cm

    d 13cm

Page 42

24 **a** 16   **b** 62

    c 24   **d** 73

25 **a** XXXVII   **b** LXVIII

    c XL   **d** LXXXI

26 **a** 27   **b** 2

    c 10   **d** 125

27 **a** 12cm

    b 2cm

    c 8cm

    d 16cm

       1, 2, 3, 4, 6, 8, 12, 16, 24, 48

28 **a** 3cm × 24cm

    b 8cm × 9cm

    c 4cm × 18cm

    d 6cm × 12cm

    e 2cm × 36cm

       1, 2, 3, 4, 6, 8, 9, 12, 18, 24, 36, 72

Page 43

29

24

1	24
2	12
3	8
4	6

60

1	60
2	30
3	20
4	15
5	12
6	10

64

1	64
2	32
4	16
8	8

120

1	120
2	60
3	40
4	30
5	24
6	20
8	15
10	12

30 **a** 1, 2, 3, 4, 6, 8, 12, 24

    b 1, 2, 3, 4, 5, 6, 10, 12, 15, 20, 30, 60

    c 1, 2, 4, 8, 16, 32, 64

    d 1, 2, 3, 4, 5, 6, 8, 10, 12, 15, 20, 24, 30, 40, 60, 120

31 **a** 2 and 4

    b 2, 5 and 10

32 **a** 2, 3, 6

    b 2, 7, 14

    c 3, 5, 15

33 1, 2, 3, 5, 7, 11, 13, 17, 19, 23, 29, 31, 37, 41, 43, 47, 53, 59, 61, 67, 71, 73, 79, 83, 89, 97

Page 44

34 a $2 \times 2 \times 2$

b $2 \times 2 \times 2 \times 2$

c $2 \times 2 \times 2 \times 3$

d $2 \times 2 \times 2 \times 2 \times 2$

e $2 \times 2 \times 3 \times 3$

f $2 \times 2 \times 2 \times 5$

g $2 \times 2 \times 3 \times 5$

h $3 \times 3 \times 3$

i $2 \times 2 \times 2 \times 2 \times 2 \times 3$

35 a 6, 9, 12, 15, 18, 21, 24, 27, 30, 33

b 14, 21, 28, 35, 42, 49, 56, 63, 70, 77
(21 circled)

36 a 12, 18, 24, 30, 36, 42, 48, 54, 60, 66

b 18, 27, 36, 45, 54, 63, 72, 81, 90, 99
(18, 36, 54 circled)

37 a 40   b 6   c 24

38 a You could multiply each number by 7

b Number of weeks = 52 × number of years

c Cost = number of chews × 5p

Page 45

39 a $2c$

b $9 - c$

c $c + 4$

d $10 + c$

40 a 6, increases by 3

b 98, decreases by 5

c 1, increases by 4

41 6, 12, 18, 24, 30, 36, 42, 48, 54, 60

42 1, 3, 5, 7, 9, 11, 13, 15, 17, 19

Problem Solving

Page 46

1 a $13 + 5 = 18$

b $20 \div 4 = 5$

c $6 \times 4 = 24$

2 a 21

b 10

c 2

3 a ×   b +   c ÷

d +   e –   f ×

g +   h ÷   i –

4 a addition   b multiplication

c division   d subtraction

5 a $47 - 16 = 31$

b $18 \div 9 = 2$

c $42 - 18 = 24$

d $56 \div 8 = 7$

e $63 - 24 = 39$

f $54 \div 6 = 9$

Page 47

6 a 24

b 42

c 10 years old

7 a 19

b 46

c 14 years old

8 a 6637

b 1946

c 1972

9 a 153

b 270

c 380

d 540

Page 48

10

	U S T V	V S T U
	U S V T	V S U T
	U T S V	V T U S
	U T V S	V T S U
T V S U	U V S T	V U T S
T V U S	U V T S	V U S T

11 ABC, ACB, BAC, BCA, CAB, CBA

12 1 + 1 + 9
1 + 3 + 7
1 + 5 + 5
1 + 7 + 3
1 + 9 + 1

3 + 1 + 7
3 + 3 + 5
3 + 5 + 3
3 + 7 + 1

5 + 1 + 5
5 + 3 + 3
5 + 5 + 1

7 + 1 + 3
7 + 3 + 1

9 + 1 + 1

13

	V-neck top	Round neck top	Collared top
White T-shirt	white V-neck top	white round neck top	white collared top
Blue T-shirt	blue V-neck top	blue round neck top	blue collared top
Black T-shirt	black V-neck top	black round neck top	black collared top

14 15, 20, 25, 30, 35
12, 16, 20, 24, 28
28 free sweets

Page 49

15 4, 6, 8, 10, **22 cubes**

16 3, 6, 9, 12, **30 dots**

17

18 0, 1, 2, 3, 4, 5, 6, 5, 4, 3, 2, 1

Page 50

19 **a**

Shape	Cubes
1	1
2	3
3	6
4	10

b 55

20 **a**

Pattern	Dots
1	5
2	7
3	9
4	11

b 23

21 **a** 69p
b £83
c £600

22 **a** £5
b 45p
c £8
d 52p
e 8p

Page 51

23
 a £44.70
 b £8.95
 c £2.77
 d £1

24
 a 1250g or 1.25kg
 b 66.5km
 c 5.5kg
 d 30km

25
 a 10.20 p.m.
 b 7.15 p.m.
 c 1.30 p.m.
 d 14:15

26
 a Monday 3 p.m.
 b £9600

Page 52

27
 a 16
 b 15
 c 6
 d 12
 e 12
 f 12

28
 a $1\frac{3}{8}$
 b 10
 c 10

29
 a −4°C
 b 9°C

30
 a $3\frac{1}{5}$
 b $\frac{2}{5}$
 c $1\frac{6}{8}$ or $1\frac{3}{4}$

Page 53

31
 a 1.55m
 b 5.48cm

32 35 cows and 28 sheep

33
 a £14 and £35
 b £108 and £252

34 72

35
 a 5, 30cm
 b 1.3, 6.5cm

36
 a 3
 b 28ml

Geometry & Measurement

Page 54

1

Shape	Number of sides	Number of vertices	Straight or curved?
square	4	4	straight
decagon	10	10	straight
rectangle	4	4	straight
circle	1	0	curved
pentagon	5	5	straight
hexagon	6	6	straight
triangle	3	3	straight
octagon	8	8	straight

2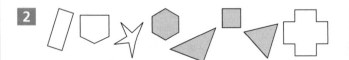

3
 a obtuse   b acute   c reflex
 d acute   e obtuse   f right

Page 55

4
 a scalene
 b scalene
 c isosceles
 d isosceles
 e scalene
 f equilateral
 g equilateral
 h isosceles

Answers continued

5 **c** and **e**

6 **c** and **e**

7 **a** kite

b square

c rhombus

d trapezium

8 **a** **b** **c**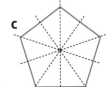

Page 56

9 **a** (2, 3) **b** (5, 1)

c (2, 6) **d** (0, 5)

10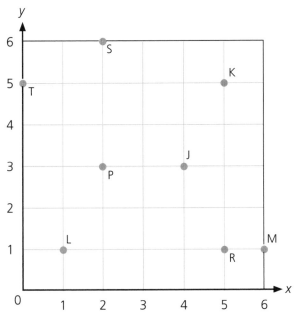

11 **a** (3, 2) (4, 4) (6, 3)

b (1, 6) (2, 8) (4, 7)

c (0, 0) (1, 2) (3, 1)

12 **a** 25° **b** 110°

c 30° **d** 160°

13 **a** square-based pyramid

b cuboid (rectangular prism)

c pentagonal prism

d sphere

e triangular-based pyramid (tetrahedron)

Page 57

14

Name of shape	Number of faces (F)	Number of vertices (V)	Number of edges (E)
cube	6	8	12
triangular prism	5	6	9
square-based pyramid	5	5	8
cylinder	3	0	2
sphere	1	0	0
cone	2	1	1

15

Shape	F	V	E + 2
cube	6	8	14
cuboid	6	8	14
triangular prism	5	6	11
square-based pyramid	5	5	10

16 **a** (3, 2) **b** (3, −3)

c (−2, −1) **d** (−4, 3)

17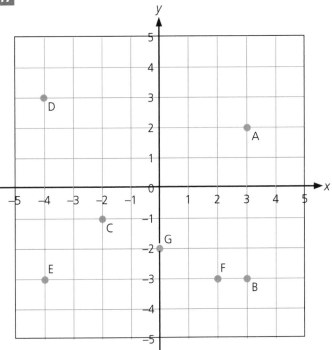

Page 58

18 a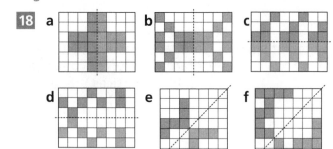

19 a (−2, 1) (−2, 4) (−1, 2)
   b (2, −1) (2, −4) (1, −2)

20 a 250°   b 80°   c 20°   d 55°

21 a radius
   b diameter
   c circumference

Page 59

22 a 400cm   b 25mm
   c 300m   d 6200m

23 a 5kg   b 20kg   c 50g

24 a 350ml   b 1l   c 9l

25 a 5200g   b 1800ml
   c 13kg   d 8.5l

26 a 3.2cm   b 1.5kg   c 3.25kg
   d 300ml   e 9.75cm

Page 60

27 a 28cm   b 27cm   c 32cm   d 64cm

28

29 a five past five in the evening
   b twenty to six in the evening
   c half past seven in the evening
   d Moviedrome
   e *The Witch's Nose*

Page 61

30 a 96cm²   b 126cm²   c 165cm²
   d 28cm²   e 40cm²   f 54cm²

31 a 12   b 6
   c 880   d 8
   e 160   f 28

32 a 1.6   b 16
   c 2   d 400

33 a 31.5cm² b 48cm²   c 150cm²   d 64cm²

34 a 242cm²   b 222cm²   c 356cm²

Page 62

35 a 20cm³   b 30cm³

36 a 60cm³   b 135cm³

37 a 180   b 300
   c 20   d 7
   e 3   f 730

38 a 50cm, 128cm²
   b 46cm, 67cm²
   c 40cm, 68cm²

Statistics

Page 63

1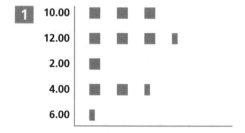

2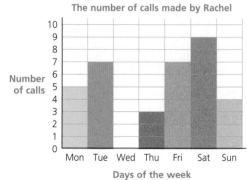

3 Tuesday and Friday

4 She may have had more time, as it was the weekend.

5 She might have mislaid the phone, run out of credit or the battery was flat, or she may have been stopped from calling anyone or not wanted to make any calls.

Page 64

6 **a** 2, 8

b 60, 160

c 25, 275, 175

7

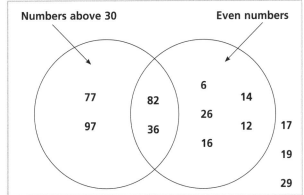

8

	Even	Not even
Numbers above 30	82, 36	77, 97
Numbers that are not above 30	6, 12, 14, 16, 26	29, 19, 17

Page 65

9 **a** 4

b 7

c 29

10 **a** frequencies 7, 9, 3 and 1

b 30–59

c 6

d 2

Page 66

11 **a** 17th   **b** 9th   **c** 2nd

12 **a** 10:45   **b** 11:00

13 12:15

14 7

15 **a** 48   **b** 90

16 5

17 **a** 5   **b** 4

18 **a** 6   **b** 6

Page 67

19 6

20 **a** 8, 7, 12

b 14, 14, 14 and 17

21 **a** estimates close to 5, 9

b estimates close to 25, 13, 19

c estimates close to 250, 130, 96

22

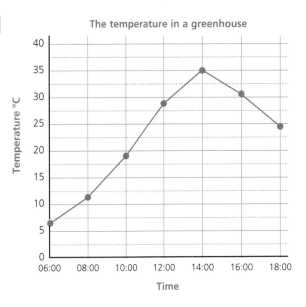

The temperature in a greenhouse

Page 68

23 **a** 9m   **b** 21m   **c** 11m

24 **a** 12m   **b** 25m   **c** 14m

25 **a** 1.5 seconds and 4.5 seconds

     b 0 seconds and 5.5 seconds

26 **a** estimates close to 1 second and 5.2 seconds

     b estimates close to 2.5 seconds and
         3.8 seconds

Page 69

27 **a** 20 minutes

     b 24 minutes

     c 13 minutes

28 13:19

29 12:45

30 **a** 702km   **b** 160km

     c 405km   **d** 275km

Page 70

31 **a** estimates close to 6.4km

     b estimates close to 4km

     c estimates close to 3.125m

     d estimates close to 2.5m

32 **a** 9   **b** 47

     c 20   **d** 58

33 119

34 **a** $\frac{1}{5}$

     b $\frac{2}{5}$

     c $\frac{1}{10}$

     d $\frac{3}{10}$

Page 71

35 **a** $\frac{5}{12}$

     b $\frac{1}{4}$

     c $\frac{1}{6}$

     d $\frac{1}{12}$

36 **a** 80°

     b 120°

     c 100°

     d 60°

37 **a** $\frac{80}{360}$ or $\frac{2}{9}$

     b $\frac{120}{360}$ or $\frac{1}{3}$

     c $\frac{100}{360}$ or $\frac{5}{18}$

     d $\frac{60}{360}$ or $\frac{1}{6}$

38 **a** 40 acres   **b** 60 acres

     c 50 acres   **d** 30 acres

Page 72

39

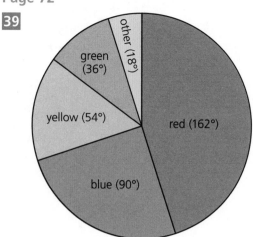

40

HOME

STENCILLING

HOME
STENCILLING

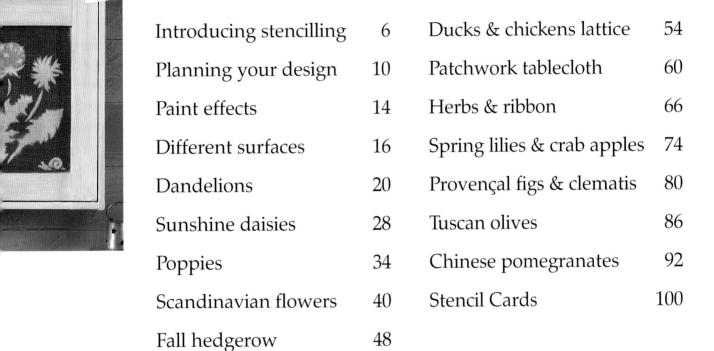

Contents

Introducing stencilling

Once you begin stencilling you will be amazed at the wonderful results you can obtain quite easily and without spending a great deal of money. This book introduces six themed projects and provides ready-to-use stencils that can be used with numerous variations in design — just follow the step-by-step features and simple instructions. With very little paint and only a few pieces of equipment you can achieve stunning results. Have fun!

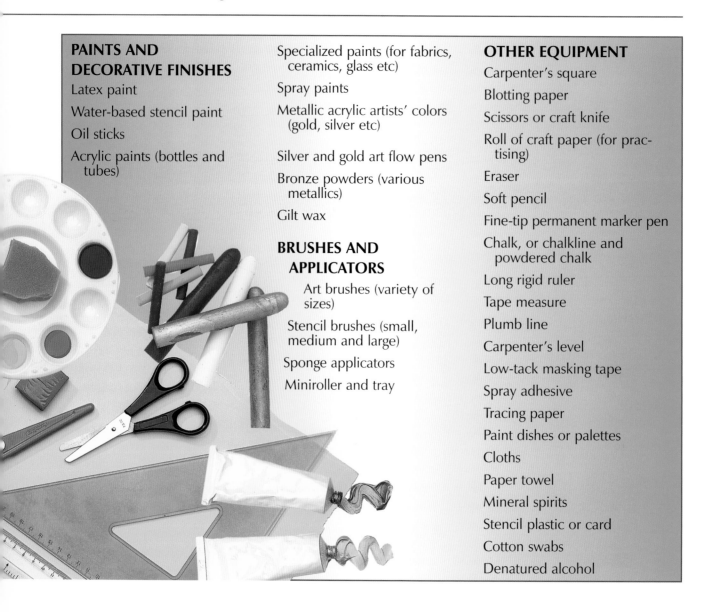

PAINTS AND DECORATIVE FINISHES

Latex paint

Water-based stencil paint

Oil sticks

Acrylic paints (bottles and tubes)

Specialized paints (for fabrics, ceramics, glass etc)

Spray paints

Metallic acrylic artists' colors (gold, silver etc)

Silver and gold art flow pens

Bronze powders (various metallics)

Gilt wax

BRUSHES AND APPLICATORS

Art brushes (variety of sizes)

Stencil brushes (small, medium and large)

Sponge applicators

Miniroller and tray

OTHER EQUIPMENT

Carpenter's square

Blotting paper

Scissors or craft knife

Roll of craft paper (for practising)

Eraser

Soft pencil

Fine-tip permanent marker pen

Chalk, or chalkline and powdered chalk

Long rigid ruler

Tape measure

Plumb line

Carpenter's level

Low-tack masking tape

Spray adhesive

Tracing paper

Paint dishes or palettes

Cloths

Paper towel

Mineral spirits

Stencil plastic or card

Cotton swabs

Denatured alcohol

CUTTING OUT STENCILS

The stencils at the back of the book are all designed to use separately or together to create many different pattern combinations. Cut along the dotted lines of the individual stencils and make sure you transfer the reference code onto each one with a permanent pen. Carefully remove the cutout pieces of the stencil. Apply 2″ (50 mm) strips of tracing paper around the edges using masking tape; this will help to prevent smudging paint onto your surface.

DUPLICATING STENCILS

Stencil plastic (Mylar) can be used; or card stock wiped over with linseed oil, which will harden when left to dry and make the surface waterproof. Place the cutout stencil on top. Carefully trace around the cutout shapes with a permanent pen. Cut along the lines with a craft knife and remove the pieces. You may prefer to trace the stencil design first, then transfer your tracing stencil plastic or onto card stock.

REPAIRING STENCILS

Stencils may become damaged and torn from mishandling, or if the cutouts have not been removed carefully, but they are easy to repair. Keeping the stencil perfectly flat, cover both sides of the tear with masking tape. Then carefully remove any excess tape with a craft knife.

LOOKING AFTER STENCILS

Stencils have a long life if cared for correctly. Before cleaning make sure you remove any tape or tracing paper that has been added. Remove any excess paint before it dries, and wipe the stencil with a damp cloth after each use. If water-based or acrylic paint has dried and hardened, soften it with water and ease it off gently with a craft knife. Then use a small amount of denatured alcohol on a cloth to remove the rest. An oil-based paint can be removed by simply wiping over the stencil with mineral spirits on a cloth. Stencils should be dried thoroughly before storing flat between sheets of waxed paper.

Getting started

MAKING A SPONGE APPLICATOR

Sponging your stencil is one of the easiest methods, but you may prefer to use a stencil brush, especially for fine detail. Using a piece of upholstery foam or very dense bath sponge, cut pieces ½–2 " (12–50 mm) wide and approximately 2″ (50 mm) long. Hold the four corners together and secure with tape to form a pad. You can also round off the ends with scissors or a craft knife and trim to a smooth finish. The small-ended applicators can be used for tiny, intricate patterns.

HOW TO USE WATER-BASED PAINT

Water-based paints are easy and economical to use and have the advantage of drying quickly. For professional-looking stencils, do not load your sponge or brush too heavily or you will not achieve a soft, shaded finish. Paint that is too watery will seep under the stencil edges and smudge. If the paint is too heavy you will obtain a heavy block effect rather than the soft stippling you require.

HOW TO USE OIL STICKS

Oil sticks may seem expensive, but in fact go a long way. They take longer to dry, allowing you to blend colors very effectively. Oil sticks are applied with a stencil brush and you need to have a different brush for each color. Break the seal as instructed on the stick and rub a patch of the color onto a palette, allowing space to blend colors. As the stencil sticks dry slowly, you need to lift the stencil off cleanly, and replace to continue the pattern.

PRACTISING PAINTING STENCILS

Roll out some craft paper onto a table and select the stencil you wish to practise with. Using spray adhesive, lightly spray the back of your stencil and place it into position on the paper. Prepare your paint on a palette. Dab your sponge or brush into the paint and offload excess paint onto scrap paper. Apply color over the stencil in a light coat to create an even stippled effect. You can always stencil on a little more paint if a stronger effect is needed, but if you over apply it in the first place it is very difficult to remove. Keep separate sponges for different colors.

Planning your design

Before starting to stencil take time to plan your design. Decide where you want to use the patterns, then work out how to position the stencils so that the design will fit around obstacles such as doorways and corners. The techniques shown here will help you to undertake the job with a systematic approach.

PUTTING PATTERN PIECES TOGETHER

1 Before you apply your design, stencil a sample onto craft paper. Mark the centre and baseline of the design on the paper and put together your pattern pieces. You can then work out the size of the design, how it will fit into the space available and the distance required between repeats.

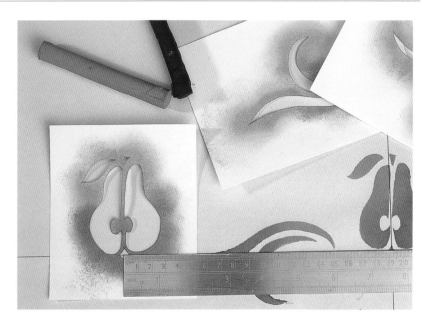

2 You can avoid stencilling around a corner by working out the number of pattern repeats needed, and allowing extra space either between repeats or within the pattern. Creating vertical lines through the pattern will allow you to stretch it evenly.

MARKING BASELINES AND HORIZONTAL LINES

Select your stencil area, and take a measure from the ceiling, doorframe, window or edging, bearing in mind the depth of your stencil. Using a carpenter's level, mark out a horizontal line. You can then extend this by using a chalkline or long ruler with chalk or a soft pencil.

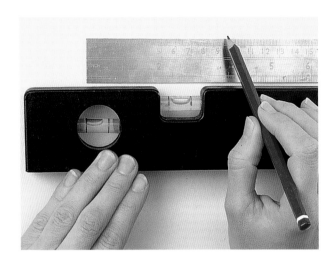

MARKING VERTICAL LINES

If you need to work out the vertical position for a stencil, hang a plumb line above the stencilling area and use a ruler to draw a vertical line with chalk or a soft pencil. You will need to use this method when creating an all-over wallpaper design.

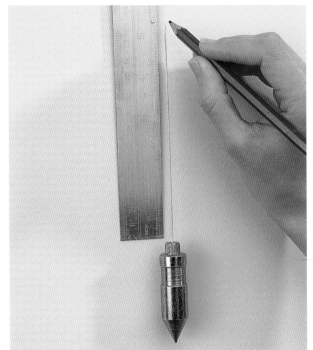

FIXING THE STENCIL INTO PLACE

Lightly spray the back of the stencil with spray adhesive, then put it in position and smooth it down carefully. You can use low-tack masking tape if you prefer, but take care not to damage the surface to be stencilled; keep the whole stencil flat to prevent paint seeping underneath.

MARKING THE STENCIL FOR A PATTERN REPEAT

Attach a border of tracing paper to each edge of the stencil. Position the next pattern and overlap the tracing paper onto the previous design, tracing over the edge of it. By matching the tracing with the previous pattern as you work along you will be able to align and repeat the stencil at the same intervals.

COPING WITH CORNERS

Stencil around corners after you have finished the rest of the design, having measured to leave the correct space for the corner pattern before you do so. Then bend the stencil into the corner and mask off one side of it. Stencil the open side and allow the paint to dry, then mask off this half and stencil the other part to complete the design.

MASKING OFF PART OF A STENCIL

Use low-tack masking tape to mask out small or intricate areas of stencil. You can also use ordinary masking tape, but remove excess stickiness first by peeling it on and off your skin or a cloth once or twice. To block off inside shapes and large areas, cut out pieces of tracing paper to the appropriate size and fix them on top with spray adhesive.

MITERING STENCIL
PATTERNS

1 When you are stencilling a
continuous pattern and need to
make a corner, mask off the stencil
by marking a 45-degree angle at
both ends of the stencil with a
permanent pen. Mask along this
line with a piece of masking tape
or tracing paper.

2 Make sure the baselines of the
stencil on both sides of the
corner are the same distance from
the edge, and that they cross at the
corner. Put the diagonal end of the
stencil right into the corner and
apply the paint. Turn the stencil
sideways to align the other diagonal
end of the stencil and turn the corner.

Paint effects

CHOOSING COLORS

Take care to choose appropriate colors to create the effect you want. Stencil a practice piece onto paper and try a variation of colors to ensure you are pleased with the result. Different colors can make a design look entirely different. Use spray adhesive to fix your practice paper onto the surface on which you wish to produce the design so that you can assess its effect before applying the stencil.

APPLYING WATER-BASED COLORS

Water-based paint dries quickly, so it tends to layer rather than blend. It is best applied by using a swirling movement or gently dabbing, depending on the finished effect you wish to create. Once you have applied a light base color, you can add a darker edge for shading. Alternatively, leave some of the stencil bare and add a different tone to that area to obtain a shaded or highlighted appearance.

BLENDING OIL-STICK COLORS

Oil sticks mix together smoothly and are perfect for blending colors. Place the colors separately on your palette and mix them with white to obtain a variety of tones or blend them together to create new colors. You can also blend by applying one coat into another with a stippling motion while stencilling. Blending looks most effective when applying a pale base coat, then shading on top with a darker color.

HIGHLIGHTING

A simple way to add highlighting to your design is first to paint in your stencil in a light tone of your main color, then carefully lift the stencil and move it down a fraction. Then stencil in a darker shade; this leaves the highlighted areas around the top edges of the pattern.

GILDING

After painting your stencil use gold to highlight the edges. Load a fine art brush with gold acrylic paint and carefully outline the top edges of the pattern. Use one quick brush stroke for each pattern repeat, keeping in the same direction. Other methods are to blow bronze powder onto the wet paint, draw around the pattern with a gold flow pen, or smudge on gilt wax cream, then buff to a high sheen.

APPLYING SPRAY PAINTS

Spray paints are ideal on glass, wood, metal, plastic and ceramic surfaces. They are quick to apply and fast drying, but cannot be blended, although you can achieve subtle shaded effects. Apply the paint in several thin coats. Mask off a large area around the design to protect it from the spray, which tends to drift. Try to use sprays out of doors or in a well-ventilated area. Some spray paints are non-toxic, making them ideal for children's furniture.

Different surfaces

RAW WOOD

Rub the wood surface down to a smooth finish.
Then fix the stencil in place and paint with a thin
base coat of white, so that the stencil colors will
stand out well when applied. Leave the stencil in
place and allow to dry thoroughly, then apply
your stencil colors in the normal way. When
completely dry you can apply a coat of light
wax or varnish to protect your stencil.

PAINTED WOOD

If you are painting wood or manufactured wood
products (MDF) prior to stencilling, seal it with
a coat of acrylic primer before adding a base coat
of latex or acrylic paint. If the base coat is dark,
stencil a thin coat of white paint on top. Apply
your stencil and, if required, protect with a coat
of clear varnish when it is completely dry.

FABRIC

Use special fabric paint for stencilling on fabric
and follow the manufacturer's instructions
carefully. Place card or blotting paper behind the
fabric while working and keep the material taut.
If you are painting a dark fabric, best results are
achieved by stencilling first with white or a
lighter shade. Heat seal the design following
the manufacturer's instructions.

CERAMICS

Use special ceramic paints to work directly onto glazed ceramic tiles, and unglazed ceramics such as terra cotta. Make sure all surfaces are clean, so that the stencils can be fixed easily. Apply the paint with a brush, sponge, spray or miniroller. Ceramic paints are durable and washable, and full manufacturer's instructions are given on the container.

GLASS

Before applying the stencil make sure the glass is clean, spray on a light coat of adhesive and place the stencil in position. Spray on water-based or ceramic paint, remove the stencil and allow to dry. If you wish to stencil drinking glasses, use special non-toxic and water-resistant glass paints. An etched-glass look with stencils on windows, doors and mirrors can be achieved with a variety of materials.

PAINTED SURFACES

Stencils can be applied to surfaces painted with flat or satin latex emulsion, oil-based scumble glazes, acrylic glazes and varnishes, and to matt wallpaper. If you wish to decorate a gloss surface, stencil first with an acrylic primer, leave to dry and then stencil the colors on top. Surfaces to be stencilled need to be smooth so that the stencil can lie flat.

FLOWER POWER

Flowers have always been a source of inspiration for artists and interior designers. Their varied forms and colors provide an endless palette of ideas for stencilling. This chapter shows a range of different flower stencils, from the humble dandelion to the exotic poppy. Each project shows how both the flower itself and its foliage work together, making a wonderful pattern to suit different rooms and styles in your home.

Dandelions

Most gardeners have a love/hate relationship with the dandelion — this flower grows and spreads like wildfire, plaguing lawns with long roots that are extremely difficult to dig up. To children, however, dandelions are heaven-sent to "tell the time" by blowing the feathery seed heads on summer afternoons. A mesh cupboard is an ideal piece for this project, giving it a "potting shed" feel. The leaves and flowers are joined to create dandelion plants growing from the bottom of the cupboard, with seeds floating above and a snail sneaking in.

PAINT COLOR GUIDE

White spray paint

DECORATING THE CUPBOARD DOORS

1 Paint the cupboard's wood sections with an all-in-one primer/undercoat in white. Paint a couple of layers of white latex on top. You may be able to get away with just one layer depending how thick the paint is.

2 Make up a wash by diluting a stone-colored latex with water. Put the color on and carefully drag it off with a dry brush to give an "old" wood effect. Work the paint in the direction of the wood sections of the cupboard, emphasizing the joints. When dry, give the wood a few coats of varnish.

3 The door knobs are stones with holes through the middle, tied on with string.

4 Paint the dandelion stencils on the mesh using white spray paint. Practise on a spare piece of mesh. If you make a mistake, mix some silver and black paint to neaten the edges.

The dandelion plants are built up by combining the different leaves and stalks (used in reverse and upside down), topped with flowers and seed heads (dandelion clocks). The seeds are in the same pattern on each side although the overall look is random.

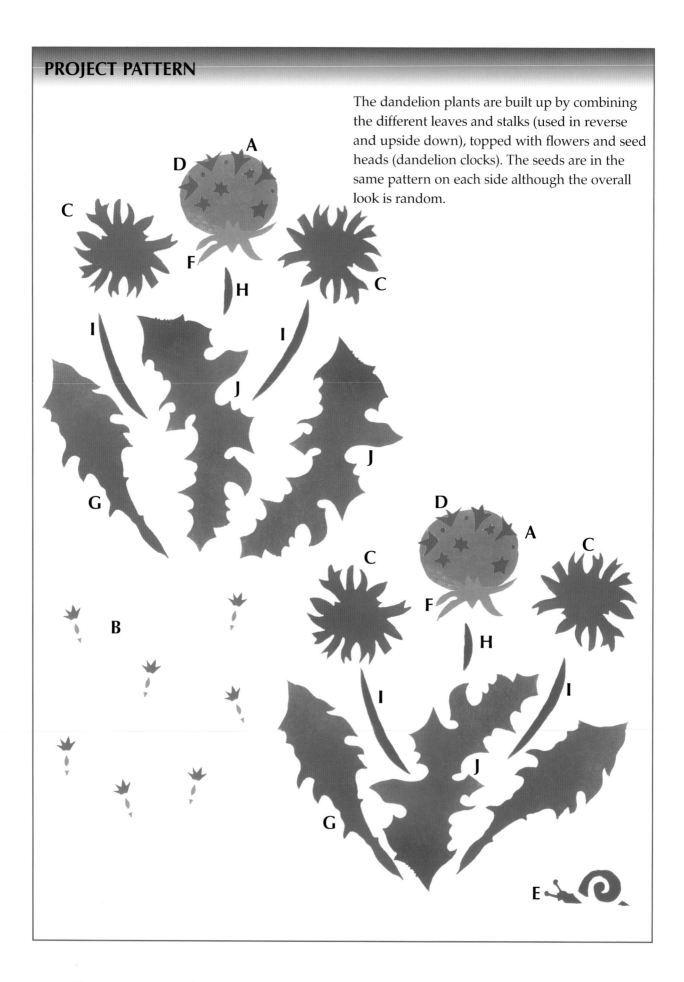

SPRAYING THE
BASE COLOR

Make sure that the stencils are fixed securely with spray adhesive, then spray the paint in thin layers to give a well-defined edge. Spray the background of the seed head (stencil D) lightly to give the faint impression of a globe before painting the individual seeds stencil A on top.

BUILDING UP LAYERS

To achieve a more opaque finish, spray lightly building up thin layers. Make sure that each element is dry before you move on to the next. Be careful not to over spray as the mesh holes can clog up easily.

CREATING THE
SNAIL STENCIL

Use the snail (stencil E) to create a trail round a pot, along the front of shelves or on top of skirting boards. A simple element in a single color can be low key or dramatic depending on the color you use and how densely you apply it.

Dandelions variations

This project provides endless opportunities for creative decoration. You can use greens and yellows to form realistic-looking dandelion plants or, as shown here using greens, turquoises and blues, choose the individual elements to build up many other designs. Do not be afraid to experiment with the different shapes as pure pattern rather than restricting yourself to the realistic growth pattern of the actual plant.

Snail trail (stencil E)

Leaf border (stencil J)

Star edging (stencil A)

Leaf circle (stencil J)

Seed head design
(stencils A, D, F
and H)

Leaf wheel (stencil G)

Snowflake motif (stencil B)

Seed head design (stencils A, D, F and H)

Flower and stalk repeat (stencils C and I)

Flower corner (stencil C)

Star medallion (stencil A)

Narrow leaf diamond border (stencil G)

Regimental seeds row (stencil B)

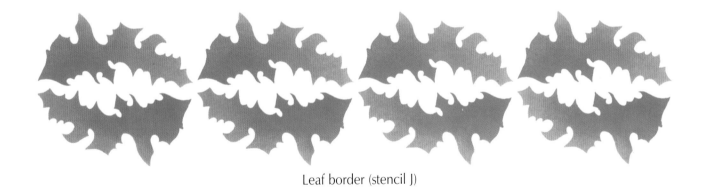

Leaf border (stencil J)

Seed square repeat (stencil B)

Sunshine daisies

This sunny daisy design seems to represent all the warmth of summer. Stencilled onto table linen these flowers will brighten any meal and bring glowing compliments from guests. Placemats could be stencilled to match the tablecloth. Stencilling onto fabric requires confidence as mistakes cannot be wiped away, but with a little practice this project is well within the reach of a beginner.

The table linen here has been painted in warm yellows, but the flowers would look equally striking in other bright colors.

PAINT COLOR GUIDE
White
Yellow
Red
Green

STENCILLING ONTO FABRIC

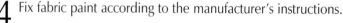

1 Wash the fabric before painting to remove any finishes. Press well.

2 When stencilling on fabric be particularly careful to use as dry a brush as possible to avoid paint seeping under the stencil. Fabric paints are available in a more limited range of colors, so mix the yellow and red paints for further warm yellows and oranges.

3 Position stem stencils B and D first before placing the flowers and leaves.

4 Fix fabric paint according to the manufacturer's instructions.

POSITIONING THE STENCIL

Use parts of the stem (stencil B) and flower stencils to make a bunch, masking areas not to be painted. Hold the stencil in place on the fabric with spray adhesive. Reposition the stencils carefully for each subsequent color you apply.

PAINTING THE STENCIL

When working on a colored fabric, paint the whole design in white before applying the colors. Allow the white paint to dry and fix according to the manufacturer's instructions before adding the colors. This gives a good background for the subsequent colors.

ADDING THE COLORS

Use a clean sponge to apply pale yellow for the petals. Let the yellow paint dry and fix it before adding more colors. Paint a rich orange-red in the centre for the stamens. Overlap the colors to effect a gradual change.

Daisies variations

The Sunshine Daisies stencils look good on walls and furniture as well as on fabric. Paint a border of flower heads in the breakfast room to complement your tablecloth. The circle of leaves is formed by overlapping a leaf stencil, taking care not to paint over the previous leaf. Try painting the flowers in different colors and flipping the stencils to create a posy.

Leaf circle (stencil C)

Daisies (stencils A, B and E)

Bunch of daisies (stencils A and E)

Daisy edging (stencil D)

Leaf border (stencil C)

Daisy and leaf border (stencils A and B)

Climbing leaves frame (stencil B)

Two daisies border
(stencils A, B and E)

Daisy border (stencil E)

Daisy chain
(stencils B and E)

Poppies

Poppies conjure up the quintessential hazy feeling of a high summer's day. In this project the combination of yellow ochre, deep purple, red and fiery orange creates a harmonious warm atmosphere. Spiky leaves, curvaceous poppy flowers with dark seductive centres, rounded seed heads, gently bending buds and bumble bees fuse to form a sympathetic union of shapes. Together the colors and shapes convey the feeling of walking through a golden field of corn, dotted with the richness of red and orange wildflowers.

PAINT COLOR GUIDE

Deep purple

Dark red

Fiery orange

PAINTING THE FRAME

1 Paint the frame with all-in-one primer/undercoat and then paint two layers of yellow ochre latex paint.

2 Mix up a wash, with the consistency of light cream, using a burnt umber acrylic and latex glaze. Gently apply the wash with big brushstrokes, working across the frame so that there is a hint of color.

3 Apply the large poppy (stencils E, G and F) in the corners of the frame and add the other elements in a random pattern. Finish the frame by painting the inner and outer edges with a rich red to give the sides definition.

In this random design the most difficult element is the poppy flower. Place stencil E first and then put stencil G carefully on top. Finish with stencil F, to complete the flower.

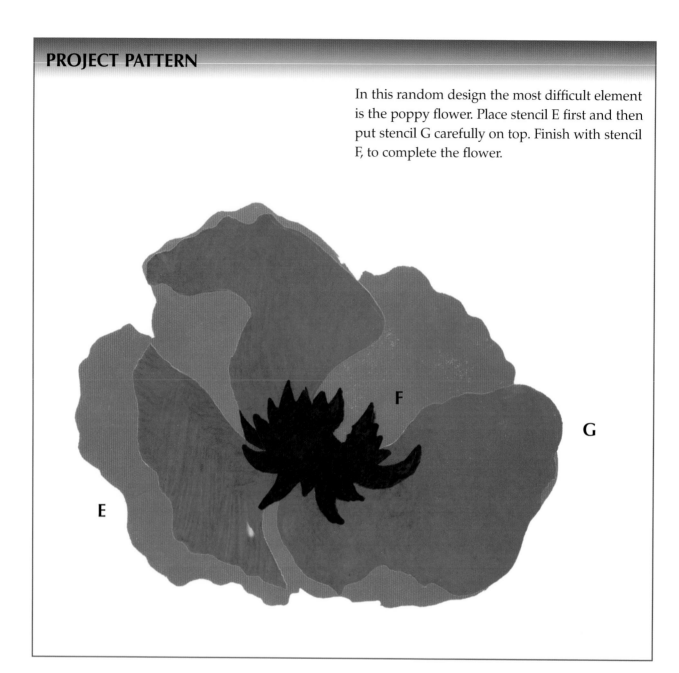

POSITIONING WITH CUTOUTS

To position the stencils make cutouts in paper and move the shapes around until you are happy with the design. Start with the larger shapes to get the pattern going and fill in the gaps with the smaller ones. Let some shapes overlap the frame.

CHECKING WITH TRACING PAPER

To create the large poppy petals apply stencil G over stencil E. Position the two parts by using tracing paper to make a drawing of the way that the shapes fit together. After stencilling the bottom shape (stencil E), slide the top shape (stencil G) under the tracing paper, then remove the paper.

KEEPING COLORS CLEAN

When using two colors within the same shape work from opposite ends of the stencil with them. Combine the colors in the middle with a different brush to keep the tones clean and clear.

Poppies variations

By adding pinks and yellow ochre to your palette of rich reds, oranges and purples you can move the design of this project towards the Orient to give a more mysterious feel or to India for a more exotic look. If you are adventurous you could make realistic poppy plants look as if they are growing out of the skirting boards or create entire poppy fields on the walls.

Seed head edging (stencil C)

Poppy centre design (stencil F)

Leaf zigzag (stencil A)

Bee repeat (stencil B)

Poppy bud and leaf tile border (stencils A and D)

Poppy head repeat (stencils E, F and G)

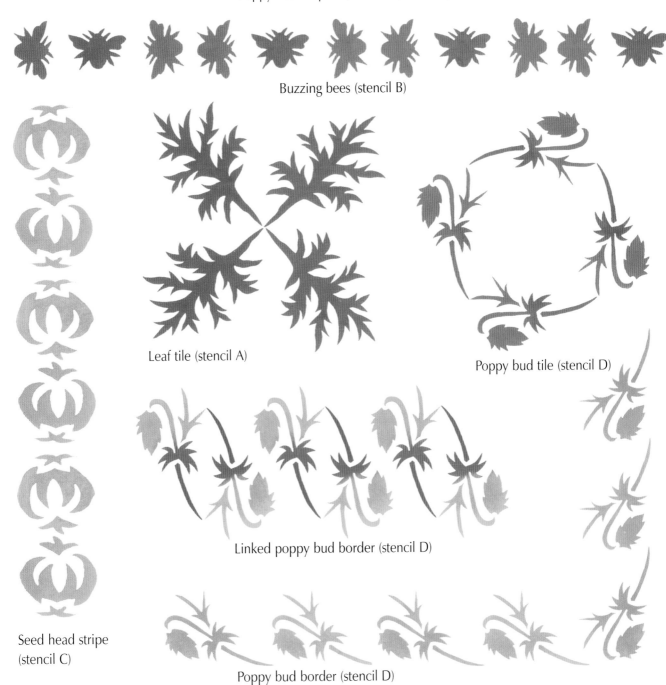

Buzzing bees (stencil B)

Leaf tile (stencil A)

Poppy bud tile (stencil D)

Linked poppy bud border (stencil D)

Seed head stripe
(stencil C)

Poppy bud border (stencil D)

Scandinavian flowers

These Scandinavian-style stencils were inspired by the architectural detail on a 19th-century Swedish house decorated in the Gustavian style. Their charm lies in their simplicity and the wonderful muted colors of the traditional Scandinavian palette. Soft grey-greens and blues combine to make this a very restful room. The border has been created by combining the leaf stencils and the wall is covered with individual tumbling leaves. To create a completely different look try painting these stencils in strong bright colors.

PAINT COLOR GUIDE

Cream

Deep blue-green

Mid blue-green

Pale blue-green

Blue-grey

PLANNING A BORDER

1 Carefully position the individual pieces to make a stylized border. The design here uses the three leaf stencils (C, D and E) and part of the hanging bells (stencil F).

2 Draw the design on a sheet of paper before you begin and note how the pieces are arranged. This will make it much easier when you come to put them on the wall.

3 Measure the distance to be covered carefully so that the pattern will fit, working each part of the design from its centre.

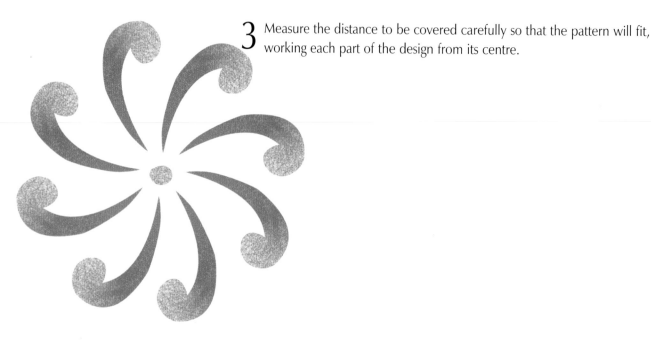

POSITIONING THE STENCIL

Mark the centre of the wall for the position of the first stencil. Measure the wall so that the design fits and you are not left without enough room to place a complete design. This will save you bending the stencils around a corner.

ALIGNING THE STENCILS

The complete design is formed by painting leaf (stencil E), flipping it over and painting it again as a mirror image, and repeating the process with leaves (D and C). This is topped with the drop shape from stencil F. Measure from a central vertical line.

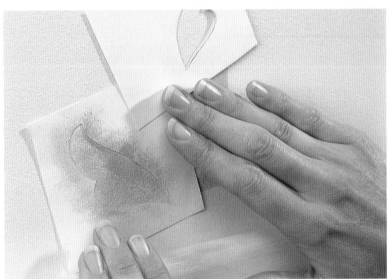

PAINTING

Use a sponge for each color. Begin with the lowest leaf, painting in the order blue-grey, dark blue-green, mid blue-green and pale blue-green, blending from leaf to leaf. This gives weight and interest to the design.

Scandinavian flowers variations

Try playing with these stencils to make interesting patterns.
You can use just one leaf stencil to create a number of
different borders. Flip the stencil over, turn it round or
overlap the images. Use the hearts and leaves to give a
"country" feel or the "comma", ribbon and hanging bells
for a more formal effect. Subtle color combinations can
make simple designs look elegant and sophisticated.

Double rope
border (stencil A)

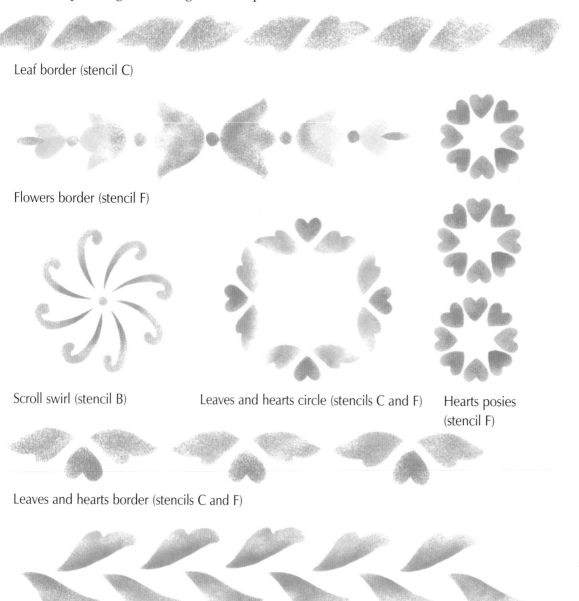

Leaf border (stencil C)

Flowers border (stencil F)

Scroll swirl (stencil B)

Leaves and hearts circle (stencils C and F)

Hearts posies
(stencil F)

Leaves and hearts border (stencils C and F)

Double leaves border (stencil E)

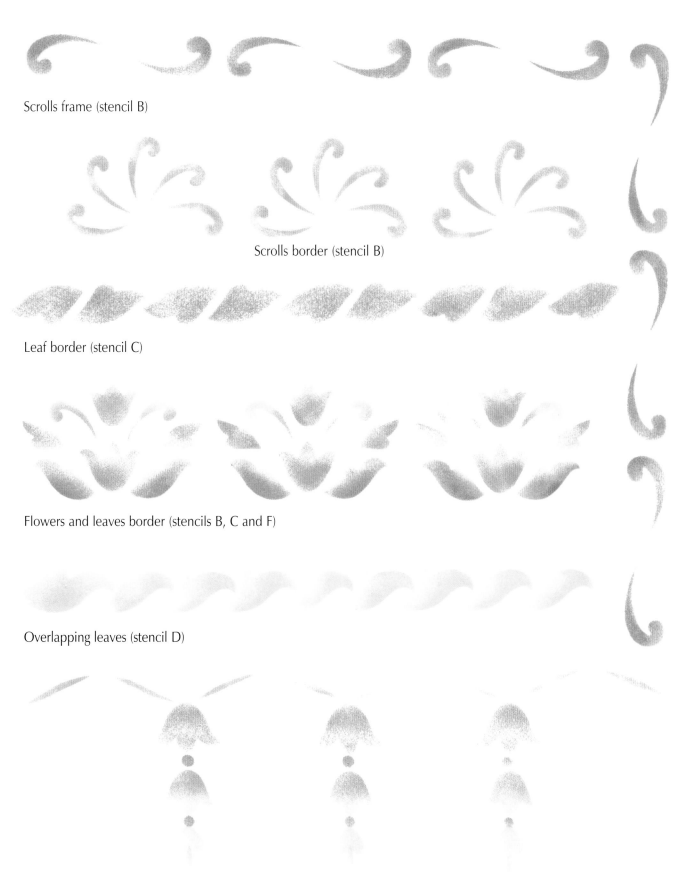

Scrolls frame (stencil B)

Scrolls border (stencil B)

Leaf border (stencil C)

Flowers and leaves border (stencils B, C and F)

Overlapping leaves (stencil D)

Rope and flower border (stencils A and F)

RUSTIC CHARM

Country life is the theme of this selection of stencils. These designs celebrate that wholesome world where nature is honoured and where simple charm is preferred to sophisticated style. The honest appeal of these patterns gives them a calming air that makes them perfect for creating a sense of tranquility. From chickens and ducks to fall berries and traditional herbs, the designs in this chapter will bring a breath of country air into your home — wherever you may live.

Fall hedgerow

Capture the richness of fall with these hedgerow stencils of rich juicy blackberries, ripe rose hips and leaves changing color from green to russet. This archway decorated with fruit and leaves trailing haphazardly around its frame perfectly evokes the season of "mists and mellow fruitfulness". The stencils are ideal for making matching, but not identical, designs in other areas of the room. Use random combinations of patterns to paint a border or highlight another feature, such as a window.

PAINT COLOR GUIDE

Yellow ochre

Plum

Bright red

Fresh green

Warm yellow

ARRANGING THE STENCILS

1 Arranging these stencils requires a little practice. Start by painting one stencil, perhaps some leaves. Then hold another of the designs to it to decide which section to paint next; choose all or part of a design, whichever looks right in that position.

2 Continue building up your design in this way. The patterns can be made to curve around an arch, make a border or trail round a corner.

POSITIONING THE STENCILS

Position these stencils individually to curve around the archway. A random arrangement will look more natural than a repetition of the same designs. Start with one of the stencils, adding all or parts of the other designs to form a pleasing arrangement.

PAINTING THE STENCIL

Paint the blackberries (stencil B) with the plum paint and the rose hips (stencil E) with bright red. Use yellow and green for the flowers and leaves. Blend and shade colors to enhance the effect. A touch of red on the edge of a leaf works well.

EXTRA DETAILS

Use parts of the stencil to add extra details and balance the design. A single flower or fruit may be all that is needed. Mask off areas of the stencil that you are not using.

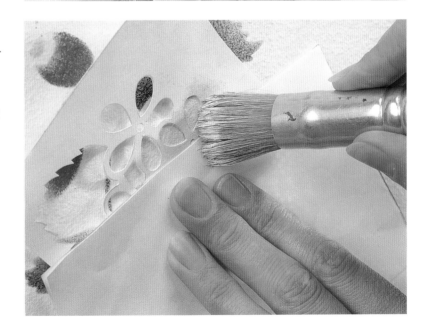

Fall hedgerow variations

The look of the hedgerow stencils can be changed by masking some details and combining the leaves from one stencil with the flowers from another. Or choose a single simple motif and repeat it, as shown in the blackberry border. The "triangular" rose hip cluster has one rosehip omitted so that it fits neatly together. Vary the intensity of the colors you use, experiment with the various stencils and colors, and find your own style.

Flower circlet (stencil C)

Flower border (stencil C)

Flower border (stencils A and D)

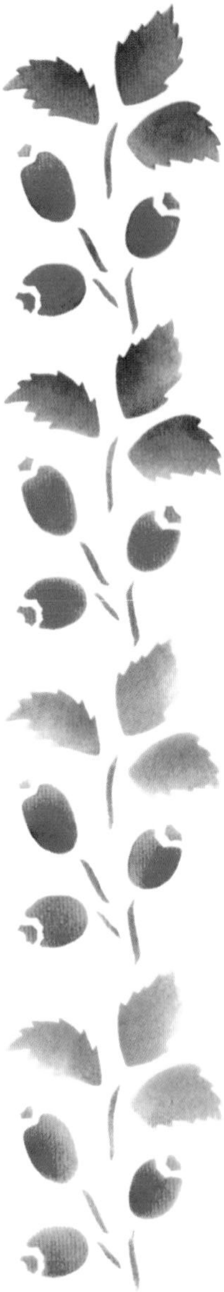

Rose hip drop (stencil E)

Blackberries and leaves (stencils B, D and E)

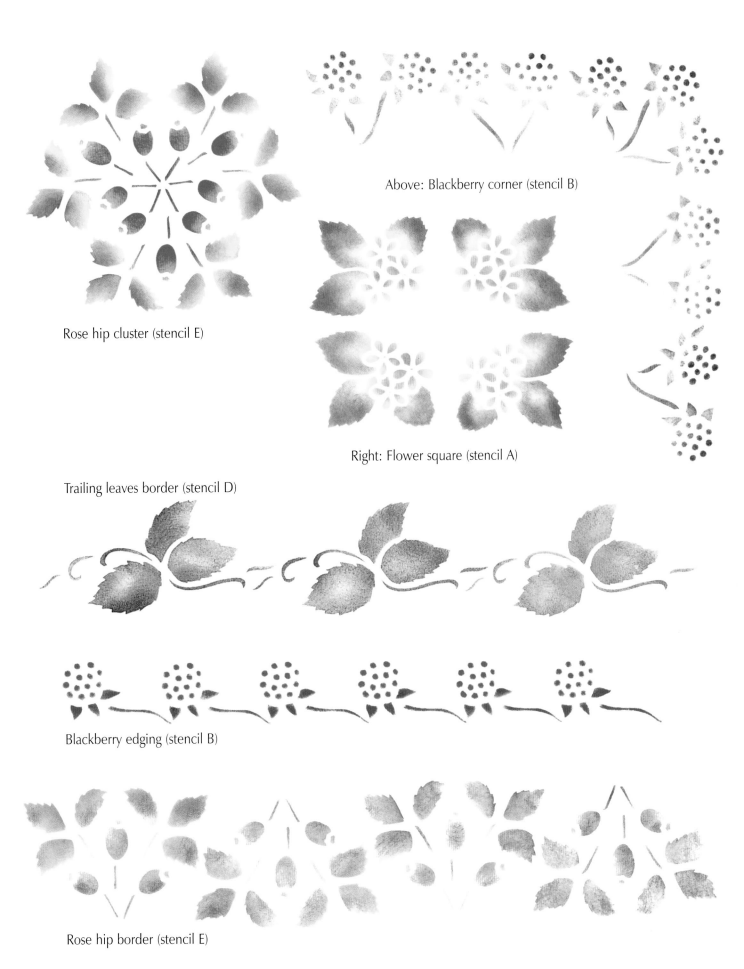

Rose hip cluster (stencil E)

Above: Blackberry corner (stencil B)

Right: Flower square (stencil A)

Trailing leaves border (stencil D)

Blackberry edging (stencil B)

Rose hip border (stencil E)

Ducks & chickens lattice

Warm, rich purple, terra cotta and earth tones conjure up a cosy farmhouse feel, with ducks and chickens in brilliant gold for a touch of sophistication. These traditional rustic colors immediately suggest a welcoming atmosphere. Just imagine the smells of freshly baked bread wafting through the kitchen and smoking log fires — utter bliss. You can use this project to create a tiled effect, transforming a town kitchen or breakfast room, or enhancing your rural surroundings, quickly and easily.

PAINT COLOR GUIDE

Muted purple
Dusky cream
Terracotta
Gold

PAINTING A TILED EFFECT

1 Paint the wall in a dark cream latex to simulate a grout color.

2 Work out the size of your tiles. Draw them out on the wall, with the aid of a carpenter's level, leaving a ⅜" (1 cm) gap in between each tile.

3 Divide a roll of masking tape lengthwise using a craft knife so that you have tape ⅜" (1 cm) wide. Stick the tape where you require the grout lines.

4 Mix up different shades of latex paint with matt glaze and paint the tiles. Remove the tape. You will be left with squares of color.

5 Stencil the lattice first (stencils E and F) and fill in the round blank space with feathers, ducks or chickens.

6 Give the whole surface a couple of layers of varnish.

The lattice tiles in the photograph on the previous page are put together as shown here ready for your choice of motif in the centre.

F   E   F

E   E

F   E   F

POSITIONING THE LATTICE

To position the lattice (stencils E and F) mark the stencil card with permanent marker to correspond with the tile lines behind. It does not matter if the stencils are not exactly straight, it will just add to the hand-painted look, but it is worth trying to keep them more or less in line.

APPLYING METALLIC GOLD PAINT

Using a metallic paint is slightly more difficult than an ordinary paint. You need to apply it more thickly to achieve an opaque look that really shines. Work on two tiles at the same time so that each stage can dry and you do not smudge the work you have just done.

PAINTING THE BIRDS

To emphasize the gold and to give the chickens and ducks depth it is a good idea to stencil some of the birds in a dark color first and work on top with gold when dry. This also helps to give the bird shapes a well-defined outside edge.

Ducks & chickens lattice variations

This project seems to suit muted earth tones best, but you could try any combination of colors. The feathers would look especially good in bright hues as an all-over wall design, floating and drifting on the surface. You could stencil the ducks and chickens in regimental rows or place them randomly as if waddling and pecking round the farmyard.

Quills border (stencil D)

Birds Frieze
(stencils A and C)

Lattice tile (stencil F)

Feathers motif (stencil D)

Birds and lattice edging (stencils A, C and E)

Lattice edging (stencil E)

Lattice frieze (stencil E)

Floating feathers (stencil B)

Above: Chicken roundelay (stencils A and F)

Lattice corner (stencil F)

Patchwork tablecloth

Red and white checks seem to conjure up the instant warmth of a farmhouse. With just a few basic shapes, combined totally at random, it is easy to create a pattern that looks a great deal more complicated than it really is. This project requires patience in planning, but the end result is incredibly satisfying — a tablecloth that is crying out for a steaming pot of tea and copious quantities of home-made cookies and jam to be set upon it.

PAINT COLOR GUIDE

Bright red
Cream
White

PAINTING THE TROMPE L'OEIL CLOTH

1 Map out freehand with a faint pencil line where you want the tablecloth to be. If you are working on bare wood, prime it. Paint the base color of the cloth in a cream-colored latex.

2 When dry load up a paintbrush with the same cream color and paint a ridge on the edge of the cloth. Do this by slightly twisting the brush outwards, away from the cloth towards the wood. Paint in a white line to finish the edge.

3 Stencil the solid red square shapes first (stencil G).

4 Fill in the empty squares at random. Stand back every so often to check that the different elements are evenly distributed.

5 Stencil a line of stitches (stencil B) along the outside edge. Finally, varnish the cloth.

The pattern in the photograph on the previos page is built up of alternating red squares and motifs of your choice in between.

G   **A**   **G**

H

F

G   **C**   **G**

PAINTING THE EDGE OF THE CLOTH

To make the cloth look more three-dimensional, paint a ridge on the outside edge and finish it off with a thin white line. This will give the illusion that the cloth is sitting on top of the table rather than painted on.

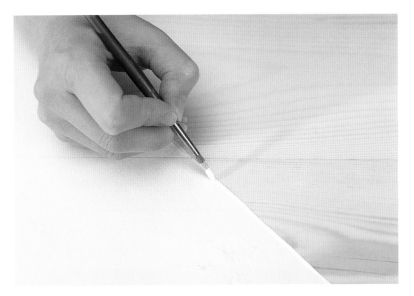

MARKING OUT THE SQUARES

Find the centre of the cloth and draw inside stencil G in pencil to mark out the first square. Draw lines across the square from corner to corner and extend them to the edge of the cloth. Mark 5¼" (13 cm) intervals along these lines. Following the direction of the first square, link the lines together to create a grid, enabling you to position the stencil card easily.

PLACING THE MOTIFS

Stencil the non-symmetrical shapes in all directions so that they can be viewed from all angles. For example, position a heart facing up in one square, down in the next, or left and right. Finally, rub out any remaining lines and put on a couple of layers of varnish. An oil-based varnish makes the surface slightly heat resistant and gives a yellow tinge, which unifies the whole surface.

Patchwork tablecloth variations

By painting the patchwork design in blue and yellow ochre you can create a softer look, perhaps lifted with just a little red for warmth. An unusual variation would be to paint a wallhanging using the double stitch (stencil D) as fringing. The motifs can be used to give impact in small areas and in more muted shades they could be used to create a Shaker-style design.

Square and heart motif (stencils A and G)

Star tiles (stencil H)

Below: Stitched heart border (stencils A and D)

Hearts stripes
(stencils A
and C)

Square and windmill blocks (stencils F and G)

Star and stitch border (stencils B, G and H)

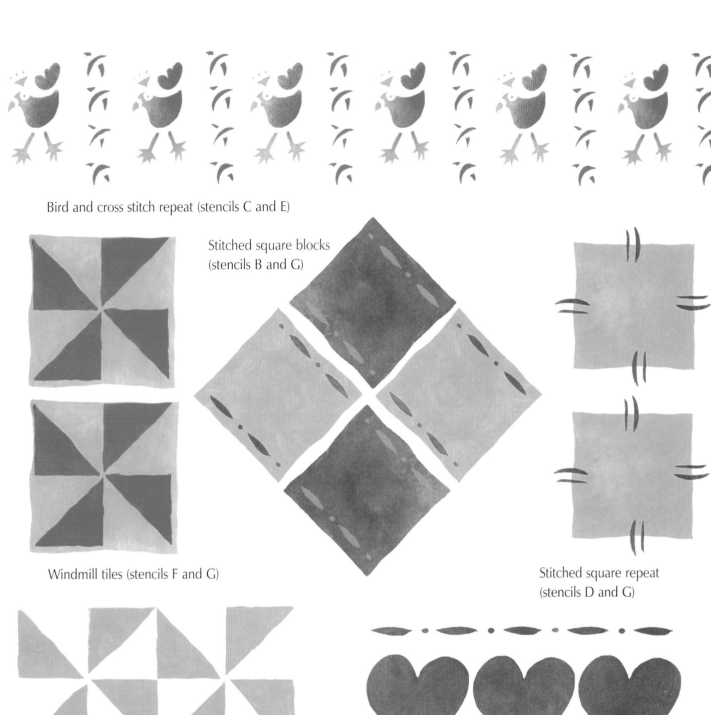

Bird and cross stitch repeat (stencils C and E)

Stitched square blocks
(stencils B and G)

Windmill tiles (stencils F and G)

Stitched square repeat
(stencils D and G)

Windmill blocks (stencil F)

Reflected hearts border (stencils A and B)

Herbs & ribbon

The calm, muted colors of sage green, clear blue and purple are ideal for creating a gentle rustic theme. Freshly gathered herbs tied together in bunches with a colorful purple ribbon and hanging from the kitchen beams to dry, conjure up the essence of country life. Sage, rosemary and thyme are all plants stored for use during the winter months for culinary purposes or herbal remedies, lotions and potions. Here they decorate the shelves and a wooden platter.

PAINT COLOR GUIDE

Cream

Sage green

Cornflower blue

Purple

DECORATING THE PLATTER

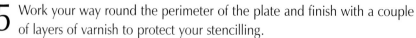

1 Paint the wooden plate with primer and then with a coat of cream latex.

2 Mix a small amount of sage green latex paint with flat glaze and apply a wash to the plate using big sweeping movements.

3 Start the stencilling with the ribbon (stencil A) and build up the herbs from the bottom. Fill any gaps with sections of the stencils.

4 Use different gradations of color to give variation and depth to the design.

5 Work your way round the perimeter of the plate and finish with a couple of layers of varnish to protect your stencilling.

The border on the plate in the photograph on the previous page is a simple repeat of this pattern; stencils are superimposed in a random manner to create the bunch of herbs in the centre.

E

F

MASKING OFF PARTS OF STENCILS

In this project the design is built up as you go along, sometimes using the whole shape of the stencil and sometimes masking off sections to fill in the gaps. Do not worry if shapes overlap — it adds to the end result and makes the herb bunch look more generous.

MEASURING FOR THE BORDER

To have a set repeat round the outside of the plate you will need to measure the design you want to use, then measure the space you want it to fit into. Simply divide the design length into the plate circumference and mark it onto the plate faintly in pencil as a guide. Use a tape measure for measuring.

GRADUATING COLOR FOR DEPTH

By graduating the paint color from light to dark within the stencil and repeating this in each subsequent shape you can achieve an undulating effect. This will give your design more visual movement.

Herbs & ribbon variations

Sage green is a color that seems instantly to suggest a country kitchen, but a much brighter blue-green is used here to good effect. The shape of the thyme sprigs allows them to be trailed wherever you wish and although the rosemary and sage are slightly more rigid in pattern they can also be placed in a multitude of designs. Bunches of herbs would look great stencilled as if hanging just below the ceiling.

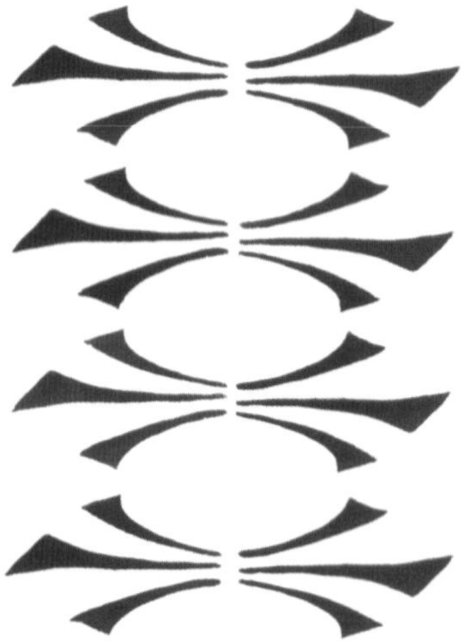

Reflected stalk frieze (stencil C)

Twisted thyme border (stencil E)

Sage leaf edging (stencil D)

Entwined ribbons border (stencil A)

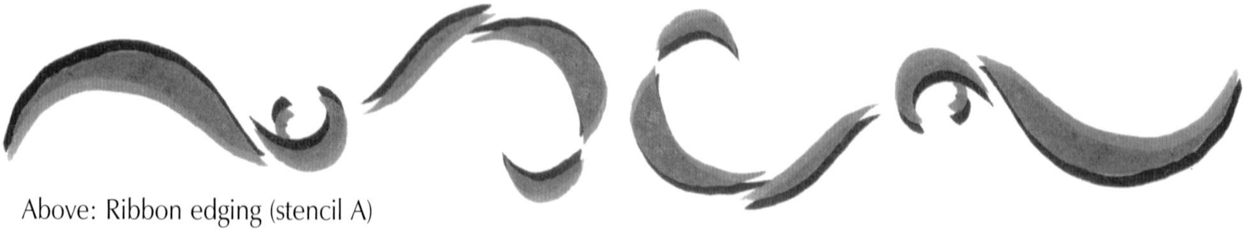

Above: Ribbon edging (stencil A)

Sage leaf border (stencil D)

Reflected stalk edging (stencil C)

Sage leaf pattern (stencil D)

Rosemary border (stencil B)

Looped ribbon
bow (stencil A)

Thyme swag (stencil F)

Thyme circle (stencil F)

Random ribbons (stencil A)

NATURE'S HARVEST

These designs celebrate the abundance of nature. The many different forms of fruits and flowers give designers a wonderful range of shapes, textures and colors to experiment with. Try a Mediterranean feel with a Tuscan olive pattern, or a touch of France with Provençal figs and clematis. Whatever the room, you're sure to find a pattern for it among these glorious shapes.

Spring lilies & crab apples

Delicate white lilies are traditionally associated with modesty and purity, but they make an effective contrast with the familiar culinary properties of acid green crab apples. To create an instant impression of peace and harmony you could use any of these stencils in different combinations. There are no hard and fast rules, so move the stencils as your space dictates. Transform a plain kitchen wall, as here, or perhaps trail the shapes over your garden furniture and containers.

PAINT COLOR GUIDE
White
Lime green
Dark green

PAINTING THE BORDER

1 First paint your wall with apple-green latex paint.

2 Carefully mark out the border using a carpenter's level and mask off the stencilling area with low-tack tape or string pinned at intervals.

3 Gently spray the backs of the stencils with spray adhesive, leave for a few minutes so the glue is not too sticky, then start to put them in position.

4 Position your stencils randomly, trying not to repeat the same motif next to itself. Place them at varying angles — even sideways or upside down. Reposition them until you are happy with the pattern.

PAINTING LIGHT ON DARK

It is usual to start with a light background and paint darker colored stencils. Here the combination of light on dark and dark on light adds to the depth of the design. To work with white use a clean sponge and dry stencil.

FADING FOR AN AGED LOOK

A fresco effect can be achieved by fading colors into the background. In this way the end result will not look so contrived and the stencilled image will look as if it has been on the wall for years.

BALANCING THE DESIGN

Placing the stencils randomly may seem an easy option, but it requires careful planning. Take the time to stand back and see that the weight of the design is level. Fiddle with the different elements in the empty spaces until one fits.

Spring lillies & crab apples variations

Instead of the cool effect of the lime-green and white combination used on the kitchen wall, try a variation. How about burgundy lilies with more muted green crab apples, for example? Use the lilies on their own or leave the crab apples cooking in rows. For a more sophisticated setting try the designs in a dining room.

One-tone bud and sprig repeat (stencils A and C)

Lily flowers border (stencil D)

Crab apple frieze in two colors (stencil B)

Lily flower and crab apple border (stencils B and D)

Crab apples and lily bud border (stencils A, B and E)

Simple linking sprigs (stencil C)

Large crab apple border (stencil E)

Twisting crab apple frieze (stencil B)

Bold flower pattern (stencil D)

Lily Art Deco design (stencil C)

Lily flower and bud repeat (stencils A and D)

Simple linking buds (stencil A)

Provençal figs & clematis

The balmy atmosphere of the South of France is conjured up by this attractive combination of luscious figs and the stately appearance of large clematis blooms. Earthy colors of dark terra cotta, purple, olive and cream epitomize fall in Provence. Create a warm and rustic look on anything from blanket boxes to archways, study walls to kitchen cabinets. The trailing nature of the clematis plant, with its star-shaped flowers and entwining tendrils, particularly lends itself to floors.

PAINT COLOR GUIDE

Deep purple

Terra cotta

Olive green

Golden cream

Dark brown

PAINTING THE FLOOR PATTERN

1 First whitewash the floorboards with a 50:50 mix of water and white latex paint. Build up in layers until you have the desired effect.

2 Position the stencil cards on the floor. Try to keep the pattern looking like it is growing so that it engulfs the surface.

3 Alternate the leaves with tendrils, flowers and figs totally at random. If you come across a good combination, repeat it, but at a good distance from the first so that you achieve a natural-looking effect. Floors should be finished off with a couple of coats of varnish.

MOTTLED LEAVES

To achieve a mottled look within each element, dab the stencil with one color, let it dry for a moment, then sponge a different color on top. This gives a wonderful uneven effect.

SHADING THE FIGS

Create graduated shading by blending into the first color while it is still wet. Start with the darker color, but do not put it quite as far as you ultimately want it to go. Then work back towards this with the lighter color.

TACKLING CORNERS

Work around corners in as flowing a manner as possible. Sometimes it helps to put an element such as a tendril in the corner to give definition. Stand back as you progress to check you are maintaining the feeling of movement.

Provençal figs and clematis variations

As a contrast to the ripening purple figs used as a floor decoration, try a more subdued color scheme. For a lighter effect combine olive green figs with creamy white clematis blooms. Perhaps you could paint the design growing along the floor over the skirting board and up the wall. The motifs could also be used as all-over hand-painted "wallpaper" designs.

Figs and tendrils border (stencils C and F)

Leaf block border (stencil B)

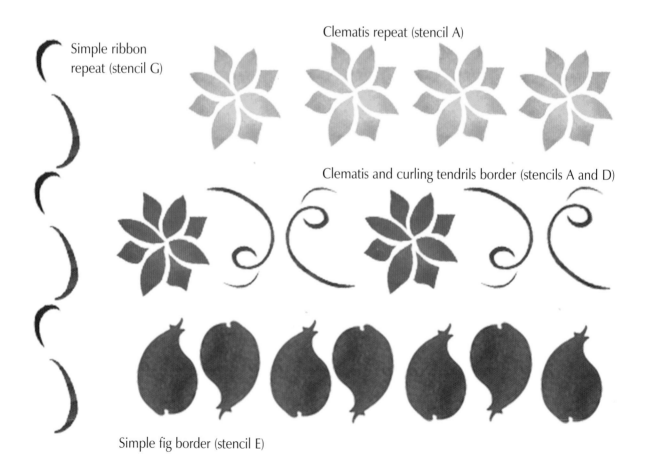

Simple ribbon repeat (stencil G)

Clematis repeat (stencil A)

Clematis and curling tendrils border (stencils A and D)

Simple fig border (stencil E)

Leaf, ribbon and fig pattern (stencils B, C and G)

Tendril edging (stencil F)

Figs and curling tendrils (stencils C, D and E)

Tendril repeat (stencil F)

Fig border (stencil C)

Tumbling leaves (stencil B)

Clematis flower border (stencils A and G)

Tuscan olives

Enjoy long summer evenings over a meal around this patio table. Stencilled with plump Mediterranean olives, it brings the flavour and atmosphere of Tuscany to your own home. The table is painted in traditional Tuscan earth colors that are rich and warm, and provide an authentic-looking background for the border of olives. It has been finished with an antiquing varnish that enhances the colors and gives it an aged look. A final coat of clear varnish protects the surface.

PAINT COLOR GUIDE

Mustard yellow

Terra cotta

Olive green

Yellow-green

Dark green

Brown

Black

PREPARING AND FINISHING THE TABLE

1 Paint the table with two coats of mustard yellow latex paint. Make a glaze using acrylic scumble and terra-cotta paint. Using a soft cloth, pick up some glaze and rub it over the tabletop to give it a textured finish. The base color should now show through the glaze. After stencilling, apply antiquing varnish.

2 Plan the positions of the stencilling by measuring carefully. Design a one-eighth segment around the table to check the fit.

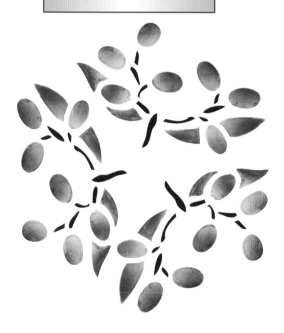

A

POSITIONING THE OLIVE STENCIL

Plan the positions of your stencils around the edge of the table top. Careful measuring at the start will ensure that you are not left with either too much or too little space to complete the circle. First work out how a one-eighth segment will look.

PAINTING THE OLIVES

Use a different brush for each color. Load the tip of the brush, removing excess paint on kitchen paper. Apply the paint by tapping or "pouncing" or, for a smoother look, press lightly on the bristles and use a circular motion.

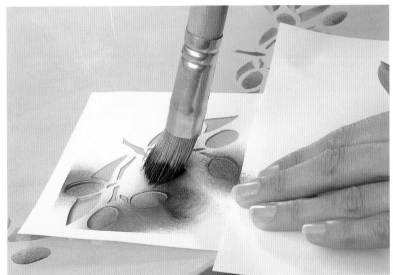

SHADING

Solid blocks of color will appear flat and heavy, so highlight one side of each olive with lighter green paint, making the olives appear round. Use two greens on the leaves to give a more realistic effect.

Tuscan olives variations

Use a single stencil to make a repeating border or combine parts of the designs for a geometric all-over pattern. To make a square tile design, paint the line stencil as a frame using the ends as a link. Position the leaf stencils inside some of the squares. The variations illustrated here show how the use of color can give quite different effects.

Leaf spray (stencil F)

Circle of olives (stencil A)

Flower border (stencil E)

Leaves edging (stencil F)

Flower border (stencil E)

Flower and broken line border (stencils D and E)

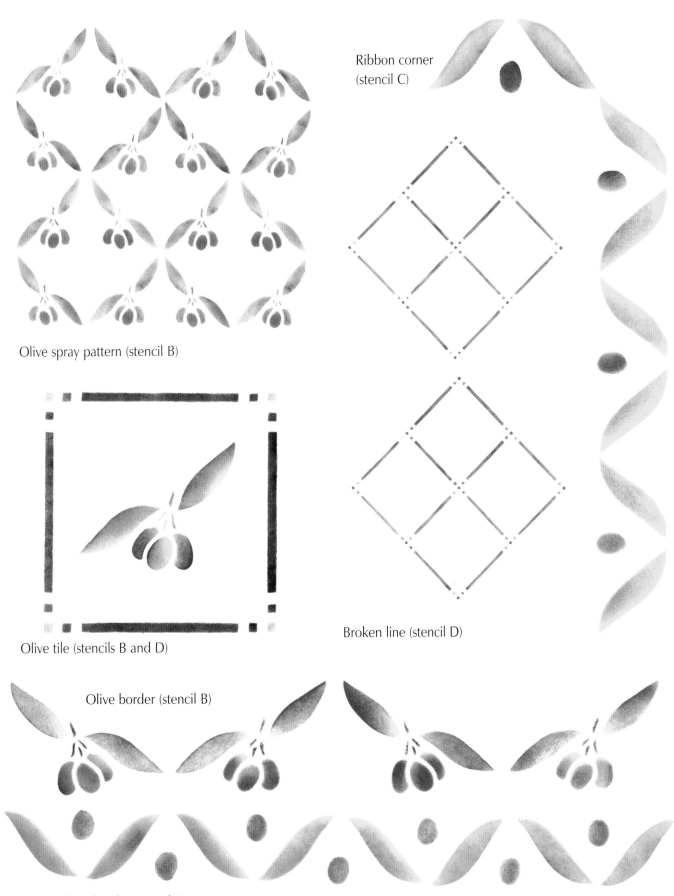

Olive spray pattern (stencil B)

Ribbon corner
(stencil C)

Olive tile (stencils B and D)

Broken line (stencil D)

Olive border (stencil B)

Olive ribbon border (stencil C)

Chinese pomegranates

The familiar Chinese willow pattern inspired this design of pomegranates with flowers and leaves, and its cool blue-and-white color scheme is particularly suitable for a bathroom. The motifs can be used throughout the room — on the walls, the laundry basket, the bath panels and even the windows. They make a dramatic-looking design when positioned closely together to create a border. Individual elements could also be used to simulate hand-blocked wallpaper using a symmetrical pattern.

PAINT COLOR GUIDE
Bright blue

DECORATING THE BATH

1 Paint the side of the bath with a couple of coats of white paint.

2 Position the solid pomegranate (stencil E) first, then put in a leaf and flower, making sure they do not touch. Then position the more delicate fruit (stencil C) at an angle. Follow this with a couple of flowers and a leaf.

3 Trace the pattern to make the repeating process simpler. Slide the stencils under the trace to the right position and remove it to paint. Draw the position of the previous repeat onto the tracing paper to align the repeats correctly.

SQUARING UP

Rather than spending hours putting plumb lines on the bath, use masking tape to stick a mini carpenter's level on the side of the bath. Then you can align and square up your stencil with the level. This makes repositioning much easier.

REVERSING THE COLOR SCHEME

If you are working with a two color scheme, it is fun to paint the combination somewhere in the room the opposite way round. Dramatically contrasting colors work well, but use the technique with similar tones for a more subtle look.

STENCILLING ON WINDOWS

A lovely finish to the scheme can be achieved, especially in bathrooms, if you take the design onto the windows. Mark off the area around the stencil with newspaper and gently spray clear or white spray — this gives a frosted or etched look.

Chinese pomegranates variations

Experiment in your bathroom with a different interpretation of the pomegranate design using aquatints of turquoise and cobalt. Ring the changes with a variation along the same theme. Choosing the right paint for the surface is always tricky. If you want to stencil an uneven surface such as wicker, use a spray paint. Spray evenly using thin coats, to keep the edges of the image well defined.

Twisting pomegranate flowers (stencil B)

Whole pomegranate border (stencil E)

Leaves repeat (stencil F)

Simple flower repeat (stencil A)

Flowing leaves repeat (stencil D)

Floating leaves
(stencils D and F)

Whole pomegranate and flowers repeat (stencils A, B and E)

Pomegranate tile design (stencil C)

Pomegranate tile design (stencil C)

Pomegranate flowers border (stencils A and B)

Published in 2005 by Murdoch Books
Pty Limited

Pier 8/9 23 Hickson Road,
Sydney, NSW 2000
Phone: +61 (0) 2 8220 2000
Fax: +61 (0) 2 8220 2558

Murdoch Books UK Ltd
Erico House, 6th Floor North
93/99 Upper Richmond Road
Putney, London, SW15 2TG
Phone: +44 (0) 20 8785 5995
Fax: +44 (0) 20 8785 5985

www.murdochbooks.com.au

National Library of Australia Cataloguing-in-Publication Data is available for this title.

Printed by Sing Cheong Printing Company Ltd. PRINTED IN CHINA.
First printed in 2005.

Dandelions

Sunshine daisies

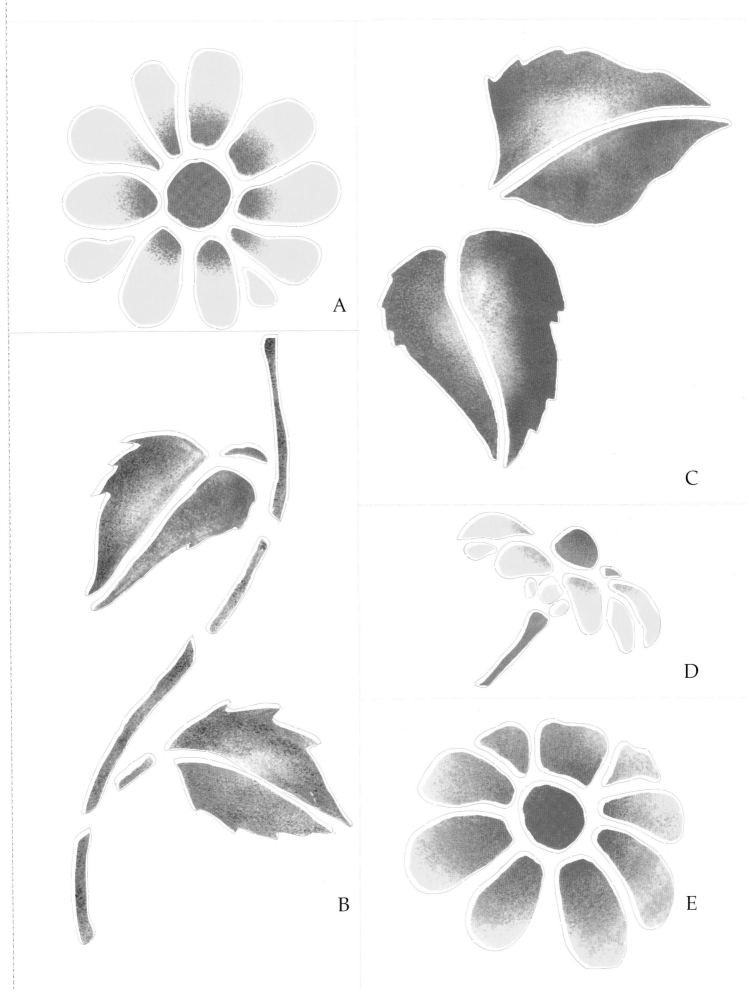

A

B

C

D

E